THE PRIVATE LIFE OF HELEN OF TROY

The
PRIVATE LIFE OF
HELEN OF TROY

By

JOHN ERSKINE

INDIANAPOLIS
THE BOBBS-MERRILL COMPANY
PUBLISHERS

Printed in the United States of America

PRINTED AND BOUND
BY BRAUNWORTH & CO., INC.
BROOKLYN, NEW YORK

CONTENTS

NOTE

After Troy, Helen reestablished herself in the home.
It will be seen that apart from her divine beauty
and entire frankness she was a conventional woman.

PART ONE
HELEN'S RETURN

THE PRIVATE LIFE OF HELEN OF TROY

HELEN'S RETURN

I

THE point of the story is that Paris gave the prize to Aphrodite, not because she bribed him, but because she was beautiful. After all, it was a contest in beauty, though Athena and Hera started a discussion about wisdom and power. It was they who tried to bribe him. They had their merits and they had arguments, but Aphrodite was the thing itself.

Her improbable remark, then, that he would some day marry Helen, interested him as a divine experiment in prophecy. It might happen or it might not. Very likely the goddess did not mean it as he thought; a wise man, even though he believed the oracle, would always wait and see.

Meanwhile he did wonder what Helen looked like. He needed travel. He might as well visit Sparta as any other place. Cassandra told him not to, but she always did. Œnone warned him, but she was his wife.

When he came to the house of Menelaos, the gate-keeper let him in, and since he was a stranger they wouldn't ask his name nor his errand till he had had food and rest. Menelaos put off a journey he had thought of, and practised the sacrament of hospitality. But when he found out who it was, he told Paris to make himself free in the house, and after polite excuses went down to Crete, as he had planned.

So they all intended well. But Paris saw Helen, face to face.

II

WHEN the war ended in Troy, with the fall of the city, Menelaos went looking for Helen, with a sword in his hand. He was undecided whether to thrust the blade through her alluring bosom, or to cut her swan-like throat. He hadn't seen her for some time. She was waiting, as though they had appointed the hour. With a simple gesture she bared her heart for his vengeance, and looked at him. He looked at her. The sword embarrassed him.

"Helen," he said, "it's time we went home."

They tell the story another way, too. Menelaos was not alone, they say, when he came on Helen in that inner room; Agamemnon was there, and others, to witness the final justice of the long war. Several who had never seen Helen, crowded in for a first and last look at the beauty for which they had fought. When Menelaos saw Helen standing there, he was conscious of his escort. Anger and strength oozed out of him, but those sympathetic friends were at hand, to see a husband do his duty. He raised the sword—slowly—not slowly enough. Then he heard Agamemnon's voice.

"Your wrath might as well stop here, Menelaos; you've got your wife back—why kill her? Priam's city is taken, Paris is dead, you have your revenge. To kill Helen would confuse those who ask what caused the war.

Sparta had no share in the guilt; it was Paris entirely, who came as a guest and violated your hospitality."

Menelaos understood why his brother was called the king of men. But later in the evening he was heard to say he would have killed Helen if Agamemnon hadn't interfered.

He had to take her to the ships for the night, with the other prisoners, but he couldn't make up his mind in what order they should set out. Not side by side, of course. He in front, perhaps. That idea he gave up before they reached the street. The emphasis on the procession seemed misplaced. He sent her on ahead to take unprotected whatever insults the curious army might care to hurl at her. But the men gazed in silence, or almost so. They didn't notice him. He heard one say she looked like Aphrodite, caught naked in the arms of Ares, when Hephaistos, her ridiculous husband, threw a net over the lovers and called the other gods to see her shame. A second man said he felt like the other gods on that occasion, who expressed a willingness to change places any time with Ares, net and all.

III

SOME other men, that night when Troy was sacked, having less cause for violence than Menelaos, showed less restraint. Ajax found Cassandra in Athena's temple, where she served as priestess—a girl lovely enough for Apollo to desire, but of no such beauty as protected Helen. There, as it were in the very presence of the goddess, he took his will of her, and went on to other business in the riot. Afterward when Athena's anger was clear enough, he admitted he had injured the woman, but asserted that he had not desecrated the temple, for Odysseus had already stolen away the sacred image, and the room, therefore, if a shrine at all, was an abandoned one. But the distinction was not likely to commend itself to the deity, and Agamemnon announced at once that the fleet would delay its homeward sailing until prolonged and thorough sacrifices had been offered, due rituals of introspection and repentance, lest the goddess should wash their sins away in cold water. Agamemnon was tender in the matter from the moment the prizes were distributed. Cassandra fell to him.

All day he stood by the priest while the flames were fed on the altars, in the midst of the respectful army, and Menelaos stood beside him—the two kings without a rival, now that Achilles was gone. At dusk they let the offerings burn down and smolder, the soldiers kindled supper-fires, and the priest said the omens so far were good.

"The sacrifices are well begun," said Agamemnon.

"For me," said Menelaos, "they are ended. It wasn't our own sins that brought us to Troy, but as you said last evening, the sins of others. Whatever errors we have fallen into since we arrived, we've had reason to regret as they occurred. If anything was overlooked, through pride or ignorance, this day of sacrifice must have made up for it, and something more. I sail for Sparta to-morrow."

"When I think of sailing," said Agamemnon, "I remember Aulis. Our setting out from that harbor cost the life of my child, offered to appease the gods. You did not object to excessive sacrifices then. It was all for you, my brother. My quarrel with Achilles I atoned for long ago, since I was in the wrong. But since at other times I may have been wrong when I thought I was right, I must now satisfy even the unsuspected angers of Zeus and Athena before this host of mine can face wind and wave and what lies between us and our dear homes."

"What you really fear," said Menelaos, "is your wife."

"Your own wife is with you," said Agamemnon, "and your daughter is safe in Sparta, no doubt looking after your affairs. We've all been looking after them. Now I must care for my people. What I really fear is the vengeance of Athena on every one of them, on you and me, on the meanest that row in the ships, for the theft of her image and the outrage to her priestess."

"Odysseus stole the image," said Menelaos, "but only because the city couldn't be taken while the image was there. For that and for some other measures in which he proved helpful, he should perhaps offer many sacrifices. As to what happened to Cassandra, I look upon it as justice, though a bit crude. Paris was her brother. The fault of Ajax was haste. He might have had her in the partition of prizes, to take home and treat as he chose, beyond the criticism of the gods and secure from the wrath of mankind, for he has no wife waiting for him."

"My wife," said Agamemnon, "has caused no scan dal in the family as yet. In some respects she differs from her sister. How many men have captured Helen, or she has captured them? Theseus, before your time, and you of course, and Paris, and Deiphobus—and wasn't there something between Achilles and her? Did Hector admire her, or was it only she that thought of him? Our special philosophies, brother, are evolved that we may live peaceably with our own past. You are in no position, I can see, to condemn the work of Ajax. Cherish your philosophy; you will need it."

"As I was saying," said Menelaos, "I sail for home to-morrow. I'm sorry we part in this mood of dispute. If staying here would do you any good, out of gratitude I'd stay. But the will of the gods is common sense, I think—or essentially so; and if your whim for prolonged sacrifices had really to do with religion, I should argue that the gods who enabled us to burn up Troy, never intended us to live here."

"You go to your fate," said Agamemnon. "I shall not see you again."

"Another mistake on your part, I prefer to think," said Menelaos, "and calling, I hope, for no ceremonial repentance."

Helen was sitting in the tent, motionless by the flickering lamp. The scented flame and smoke of the tripod went up before her face, and made him think of goddesses and altar-fires. Why was she there? Had she been there all day? Out at the sacrifices he had imagined her humbled among the other captives, feeling at last the edge of retribution. She might have stood up when he came in.

"To-morrow we sail for Sparta."

"So soon?"

"Is it too soon? You prefer Troy?"

"Not now," said Helen, "and you remember I never had much preference for places. But so many ships and men to get ready in a day! You were longer in starting when you came—with more reason for haste, I should have thought. Why, there must be sacrifices, there are gods to think of, the wide dark ocean, the ghosts of so many dead to quiet before we go."

"The dead are at peace and the gods are satisfied," said Menelaos; "we've given the whole day to sacrificing. The ocean remains wide and dark. Agamemnon will continue the sacrifices for that and for some other things prayer can not change. We have had words about it and parted. He and the host will stay a while longer, I go home to-morrow with my men and my captives."

With her, he meant. He didn't know how to say it. Not "with my wife and my captives." He hadn't the courage for "you and my other captives."

"Menelaos," she said, "of course I will share the journey with you, however unwisely you undertake it. But you are wrong, and your brother is right. Those who are conscious of wrong-doing need time for regret and for remorse, and those of us who are conscious of no wrong-doing, we most of all should offer sacrifices against our pride. You have your old common sense, Menelaos, an immediate kind of wit, but you still lack vision. If you had more vision you would be more conventional."

"If I hear you," said Menelaos, "you are advising me not to depart from established rules of conduct?"

"That is my advice," said Helen.

"I am overtired and my head refuses to serve me," said Menelaos. "Will you return to—whatever place you have just come from, or shall I leave this tent to you? We start early in the morning."

IV

THE wind was against them, and the men were at the oars. Menelaos sat near the helmsman, and Helen before him, her face bare to the wind. The rowers looked up at her, not as in anger at one who had brought on them war and labor, but curiously at first, then with understanding and awe, as though there were a blessing in the boat. Menelaos watched the change in their gaze, and wondered why he had come to Troy, anyway—and remembered why.

Helen shifted her position, for the first time in hours, and looked in his eyes. The oarsmen looked up at him, too; they forgot to row.

"Menelaos," she said, "you should have offered sacrifices. There is something very strange about this boat."

"On the contrary," he replied, "the boat is perhaps the only thing here which is beyond criticism. The wind is unfavorable, but the men row well, except when you distract them."

"In Troy at this moment, or somewhere along the shore," she said, "Agamemnon offers up prayers which I dare say will be effective; he will doubtless reach home. Our own prospect seems to me uncertain. You know my point of view—I have no love for adventure unless I know where I'm going."

"We are going to Sparta," he said.

"I fear we are not," said Helen.

"We will hold to the course," said her husband, "and unless the stars are disarranged in this much troubled world, we shall arrive in Sparta in a week. That will be excellent time, don't you think?" he asked the helmsman.

"It took us longer to reach Troy on the trip out," said the helmsman.

"When I went to Troy," said Helen, "it took only three days, but that was an exceptional voyage."

Thereafter the rowers bent to the oars and the helmsman read the sun and the stars. At first Helen would look at Menelaos from time to time, serene enough, but as though she could say something if it were worth while to do so. After many days she only sat motionless, gazing far ahead across the sea, and the oarsmen kept their patient eyes on her, as though she and they were faithful to something Menelaos could not understand. He passed the time feeling lonely, and wondering whether the water and the food would hold out.

"Ah, there is Sparta at last," he said.

"I doubt it," said Helen.

As a matter of fact, it was Egypt. Helen walked ashore on the narrow bridge the sailors held for her, as though one always landed in Egypt. The wind died completely. The weary men set up the king's tent and shelters for themselves, and went to sleep. Menelaos could not remember that he had given orders for disembarking, but he wasn't sure and didn't like to ask.

"This famous land is more interesting than I had thought," said Helen some weeks later. "In my afternoon walks I have met several of the natives, and they

seem to have reached here an average of culture somewhat above our best in Sparta, don't you think?"

"Helen, you exasperate me," said Menelaos. "I'm not
here to tour the country nor to compare civilizations."

"Of course you aren't, nor I either," said Helen, "and
when you are ready to sail you have only to tell me.
Meanwhile Polydamna, the wife of that substantial man
who sold you the food for our next voyage, is teaching
me her skill in herbs and medicines—a good skill to have
in any house, and here they all seem to have it. Unless
you offer sacrifices in the next few days, I shall learn
much of what she knows."

"I will make no more sacrifices," said Menelaos. "The
wind will rise of itself."

"Then I shall learn it all before we go," said Helen.

After a fortnight or thereabouts, she saw him one
day coming from the house of Thonis, Polydamna's husband, with a small lamb under his cloak. While he called
the men to a quiet spot and sacrificed the animal, she kept
herself discreetly in the tent. Menelaos found her there.

"Be prepared to sail to-morrow," he said, "in case a
wind should rise."

She was ready, and the wind rose, but it turned out
to be only a frail breeze, young and short-lived. As they
reached the island of Pharos it died altogether.

"Oh, well," said Menelaos, "there's a good harbor
here and a spring of fresh water. We'll put in till the
wind freshens, and fill the casks."

Helen walked ashore on the narrow bridge the men
held for her, as though one always landed in Pharos.
There wasn't a living thing on the island except a crab
or two that would venture out of the sea. After twenty

days the food gave out, and the men crawled along the stony shore, trying for fish with a little cord and bare hooks. All those days Helen walked, composed and gracious, in the smoothest paths she could find among the rocks, or sat near the brow of one modest cliff, watching the purple waters and the gulls and the far sky-line. Menelaos avoided his men and wandered alone, at the other end of the island from Helen. But she was not surprised, so far as he could see, when he strolled at last up to her position on the cliff.

"I'm thinking of going back to Egypt," he began. "These men need heartier food than they can find here, and we could row to Canopus in a day."

"If you are asking my advice," said Helen, "I can only follow your own best judgment. As you say, we seem to need food."

"At times, Helen, you irritate me," said Menelaos; "any fool would know we must go back to Egypt. I wasn't asking your advice. In fact, I ought to have gone back long ago."

He was prepared to tell her why he hadn't gone back before, but she annoyed him by not asking. He turned and saw three of his men, wan and hungry, and the helmsman with them, waiting, as it seemed, to say something unpleasant.

"Menelaos," began the helmsman, "we have followed you so long that you must know we are faithful, but we've come to ask you now if you've lost your wits. Do you enjoy suffering yourself, or do you like to see us suffer? You keep us on this island to starve, while there is food in Egypt, within one day at the oars, if we had our strength. A few hours longer here, and we shall be too feeble to launch the boat. Waiting for a wind, you say. But if it came now, there's not food enough to keep us till Sparta; we can't fish as we sail."

"I forgive your bad manners because of your hunger," said Menelaos, "but as it usually happens in such cases, your advice comes late and is therefore superfluous. I had already decided to return to Egypt for supplies, and we shall start at once. Get the boat ready. . . . Did I make myself clear? Launch the boat. . . . Oh, you have something more to say?"

"Yes, Menelaos," replied the helmsman. "When we reach Egypt we shall make proper sacrifices to the gods, that we may return home in safety. We would have sacrificed at Troy, with our fellows, but you commanded us to come away. Now that we have suffered your punishment with you, we will obey you no longer in this matter, but only the gods. Clearly it is the fate of none of us to see our friends again unless we offer hecatombs to the deathless who keep the heavens and the paths of the sea. No doubt we should have perished before this had there not been with us our lady yonder, your wife, to soften the anger of the gods—herself immortal in our eyes, reverent and careful toward those above who give life or withhold it."

"It might be well," said Menelaos, "to offer further sacrifices at this time. I had considered that also, but there is nothing here of any value to sacrifice. In Egypt, as you suggest, we can secure rich offerings, and I had already resolved to do so at the earliest convenient moment. You may now launch the boat—unless, of course, there is something further?"

They hastened down to their fellows, and Menelaos turned toward Helen.

"I hope you won't keep us waiting. This talk has somewhat delayed my plans."

Thonis gave them food to store in the boat, and cattle for the sacrifice, with bowls of dark wine. In the sight of them all Menelaos drew the pitiless knife with certain flourishes of irritation across the throats of t e victims, and they fell gasping to the ground. Then he turned the wine from the bowls into cups, and poured it forth, and prayed in an incisive voice to the gods who live forever:

"O Zeus, most glorious, most great, O Athena, wise and terrible, O all ye immortal beings! Now do your works in the light, that men may look on justice. Punish the guilty and reward the good. Who among us have sinned against you, let them starve on the sea rocks or drown in the waters. But those who with pure hearts have done your will, bring us soon to our own people!"

And the wind blew them all safe and sound to Sparta.

V

"Menelaos," said Eteoneus, the old gate-keeper, "I've hoped for a few minutes of your time ever since you came home. You've been absent a long while, and I dare say you'll want a report of the household."

"Nothing wrong, is there?" said Menelaos.

"Orestes has been here."

"Oh—my brother's son," said Menelaos.

"Yes," said Eteoneus, "and I might add, your wife's sister's son."

"What do you mean by that?" said Menelaos.

"I mean," said Eteoneus, "I had some doubt whether I ought to let him in."

"It seems to me," said Menelaos, "you imply something rude about my wife's relatives."

"To tell you the truth," said Eteoneus, "I had no idea, until you returned, that you still counted your wife among your relatives."

"You forget yourself," said Menelaos.

"No, Menelaos," said Eteoneus, "it's an awkward subject, but we'll have to face it. I have to, at any rate; I'm partly responsible. When Paris came, I let him in. What happened afterward we all know—at least, we know the events, but some of us are at a loss to interpret them. You entertained Paris, of course, without question as to what he came for, and he stole your wife and whatever else in the house was portable. Naturally you went off

for your revenge, and I may say that none of us who
stayed at home expected to see Helen again, certainly
not restored to your esteem. If you would explain the
new situation to us—give us at least a hint as to what
our attitude should be toward her, it would relieve what
is at present an embarrassment to your domestics.

"You were about to speak of Orestes," said Menelaos.

"I was," said Eteoneus. "When you went away, you
told me to look after the house with peculiar vigilance,
since your strongest men were with you, and your daughter Hermione remained here, with considerable treasure
still in the vaults. Then Orestes appeared. Perhaps
I should have asked him in, like any other stranger, and
found out his errand afterward, but in your absence I
couldn't take the risk. I kept him out until he would
say who he was. He may tell you of his displeasure."

"If there's one thing I dislike," said Menelaos, "it's
a family quarrel. I hope you didn't come to words?"

"I fear we did," said Eteoneus. "He wanted to know
what had come over this house, anyway, that all virtue,
even the most elementary, had deserted it. He suggested,
as I recall, that the stench of our manners must sicken
the gods. He went into some detail which I shan't repeat; in outline, he noticed that having begun with a
comparatively excusable slip, such as the infidelity of
your wife, we had sunk at once to a point where we were
no longer hospitable. I assured him that with us, as
with other civilized people, nothing was more sacred than
the rights of a guest, but that recently we had become
interested in the rights of the host, also, and that since
these had been ignored once in this house, we were a bit
nervous about good-looking and anonymous young men;

in these upset times we felt that unusual caution on our part should not be misinterpreted."

"I see nothing in that speech to insult him," said Menelaos.

"Well," replied the gate-keeper, "that isn't all I said. When he made that remark about your wife, I felt that loyalty to the house compelled me to say something. I inquired after his mother's health."

"That's sometimes done," said Menelaos, "even among the polite."

"I mean," said the gate-keeper, "I asked him whether it wasn't more delicate to leave your husband's roof before you betrayed him, than to be false by his own fireside while he happened to be absent. Orestes got the point—that's why he was angry."

"If Orestes understood you," said Menelaos, "it's more than I do."

"I suppose you haven't heard," said Eteoneus, "but all Sparta knows the scandal. Your sister-in-law Clytemnestra—your double sister-in-law, I might say, your wife's sister and your brother's wife—has been living with Ægisthus ever since Agamemnon went to Troy. It's hardly worth while for him to come back."

"There! I never liked her!" exclaimed Menelaos. "I'm shocked but not surprised, except for the man. Ægisthus will regret his daring. My brother will come back. He may not be wanted, but he will return all the more surely for that. He has had considerable practise recently in dealing with men who steal other people's wives."

"What Sparta is curious about," said the gate-keeper, "is whether he has had enough practise in dealing with

Clytemnestra. She's a formidable woman, even in her innocent moments, and she's making no secret of her present way of life. She thinks she is justified by something Agamemnon did. Of course she doesn't doubt, any more than you do, that he'll return. It's thought she has a welcome waiting."

"This is terrible!" groaned Menelaos. "But after all it may be only gossip. Women so beautiful as those sisters pay for their gift in the malicious rumor of envy. Really, Eteoneus, I don't wonder that Orestes was angry."

"I don't wonder myself," said Eteoneus, "but angry or not, he denied nothing. How could he? These rumors that spread about beautiful women are often malicious or envious, as you say, but they're rarely exaggerated."

"That's digression we needn't discuss," said Menelaos. "So Orestes went home? Frankly, Eteoneus, I should like to hear his side of this story."

"You may, easily enough," said the gate-keeper, "for he's been here right along, at regular intervals, and unless his habits change he's due in a day or so."

"I thought you didn't let him in?"

"I didn't, but he never asked permission again—he just came in. I ought to add that he came always to see Hermione, and she arranged it somehow, I never knew just how. She doesn't like me much more than he does."

"I can't believe anything scandalous of my daughter," said Menelaos, "and you made a grave error in introducing the idea. I have an impulse to question your judgment as to these other reports. Of course I've been away a long time and she's now quite grown up, but her character seems to me essentially unchanged. I've always thought her propriety itself."

"So do I, so do I," said Eteoneus, "and when it comes to the conventions, Orestes is rather strait-laced. It often happens that way, I've noticed—the children go in for correct behavior. Especially when they are not so good-looking."

"My daughter is said to resemble me," said Menelaos, "and I believe she and I understand each other. But if you agree that their meetings were entirely proper, what on earth are you talking about? Why didn't you let him in, in the first place? They were intended for each other, before our family life was upset; now that we've returned, I dare say they'll be married shortly, if they wish to be."

"Menelaos," said Eteoneus, "it's a difficult thing to explain to one who hasn't followed my profession. I'm a family gate-keeper, and the sense of responsibility makes me alert to what I let in. When I opened the gate to Paris, I had a presentiment that love was entering, and instinct told me that the entrance of a great passion would disturb your home. You did not feel the danger. Now Orestes, I'm quite sure, brings with him some new ideas. If you realized what it would mean to your house, to let in new ideas, you'd be on your guard."

"Eteoneus," said Menelaos, "I've heard a good deal of oratory since I left home, and though I'm no critic in such matters, I've become sensitive to possible innuendo in the spoken word. Much of what you have said sounds to me like diplomatic insult."

"I may have overstepped my intention," said the gate-keeper, "but I did want to rouse you to a problem which only you can solve. We are all loyal to you but we don't know where we stand. It used to be that a wife who deserted her husband and children was in disgrace, if possible was punished. You thought that way when you sailed for Troy. We at home here have prepared all these years to cheer your lonely grief as well as we might, if ever you came back to your—"

"Didn't you say something like this before?" asked Menelaos. "You repeat yourself and you wander from the subject. I thought you wanted to give an account of the house since I left it?"

"That's just what I'm doing, Menelaos," said the old gate-keeper, "and if I go at it in a roundabout way, it's only to be tactful. I'm trying to say respectfully and harmlessly that there are some dangerous new ideas abroad in your household, and I want to find out whether you know about them and dislike them, or whether you share them. I'm terribly afraid you share them, and if you do, I suppose I ought to leave you, old as I am, for I'm too old to change. The reason I suspect you've picked up some of these new ideas is—well, when the ship was sighted we learned that you weren't to be lonely; Helen was coming back with you. That was a new idea, Menelaos. But we got used to it, and we rehearsed what we thought would be respectful manners toward the repentant captive brought home in disgrace. But she doesn't seem aware of any disgrace, and she isn't repentant. She doesn't behave—neither do you, in fact—as though she were a—"

"Look here, Eteoneus," said Menelaos, "I've taken all I'm going to from you. You pretend to have household business on your mind, and then you pretend to have damaging news of Orestes, which turns out to be more to your discredit than his, but what you really want all along is to manhandle my wife's reputation. I'm home now, and I'll run the house myself. You get out where you belong, and watch the gate. . . . Here, wait a moment! If the madness comes on you again to talk about Helen, do it where no word of yours will reach me. You wonder why I didn't kill her. Well, she was too beautiful. You don't resemble her in the slightest. Be careful!"

"The gods be praised, Menelaos," said the gate-keeper, "you talk now like your old self! May I go on with what I was about to say?"

"Finish up with Orestes, and get out," said Menelaos.

"I'll have to go back a ways to pick up the thread," said Eteoneus. "Oh, yes. We talked it over, of course, with the men on the ship, and they answered as though we were demented; even to them who have lived through Troy and its miseries, Helen seems altogether admirable. We try to get a clue from you, but though you are at times, if I may judge, somewhat embarrassed, and though you are irritable now that I have ventured to raise the question, you too seem to accept Helen as the unshaken authority and inspiration of your home. And here's where Orestes comes in. I used to believe Hermione looked at things in the old fashion. She was rather pathetic, I thought, circulating stories about her absent mother, stories which if we were deceived by them would make Helen out quite innocent, rather a victim than—well, we'll leave it there. I admired the daughter's loyalty, though it took a fantastic form, and I was sure, of course, she didn't believe her own yarns. But now Orestes has put ideas into her head which once would have troubled you. I had a talk with her one day about him—told her what was going on between Clytemnestra and Ægisthus, and warned her against compromising herself with that

branch of the family. If you'll believe it, she actually
defended Clytemnestra. I could guess she had the argument from Orestes. Though her aunt wasn't doing right,
she said, Agamemnon hadn't done right, either; he asked
her to send their youngest daughter, pretending he had
arranged a marriage with Achilles, and when the delighted mother got her ready, and safe to Aulis, he killed
the child as a sacrifice to the winds, so the fleet might
sail. After that, Hermione asked, what loyalty did Clytemnestra owe to Agamemnon? And I couldn't think
of the reply I wanted. I did say that Clytemnestra's
conduct wasn't sanctioned by religion, but sacrifice was.
She laughed at me. There you are, Menelaos! I call
that dangerous. If you hadn't changed, you'd thank me
for putting you on your guard."

"Now that you've got to the point at last," said
Menelaos, "I don't mind telling you I have indeed
changed. I'm not afraid of new ideas as I once was, and
as you still are. We've been away a long time, we've
seen many countries and other people, and we must have
broadened. Before I went I wasn't interested, for example, in Egypt, but it's a remarkable country, and the
people know a lot more than we do. And we've been
through the war, you should remember. Nothing can be
quite the same again. When your emotions have been
stretched in unusual directions for a protracted period,
you discover that your ideas have changed, and not
necessarily for the worse. Those who go to war seem
to have more new ideas than they who stay at home. I
won't say I like these ideas of Orestes, but they don't scare
me. Before I went to Troy, if you had told me that
Achilles would give back Hector's body to be buried by

his relatives, and would stop the war for twelve days so the funeral would not be interrupted, I shouldn't have believed you, but that's what he did. When Helen went off with Paris, I followed to kill them both. Now here she is home with me again. You can't get over it. It's the one new idea you've had in twenty years—your handsome surprise that my wife is at home and not in the cemetery. I'm rather surprised myself, but not so much as you are. I can't explain it—I can only say, with you, our ideas change."

"The parallel between Hector's corpse and your wife escapes me," said the gate-keeper, "but I gather, Menelaos, that you think a great deal of good has come out of the war—not for the Trojans, I take it, not for Hector, not for Patroclos nor for Achilles, but for you. The logic of your position, I suppose, is that your wife did you a good turn when she ran away with another man."

"I don't know that my gate ever needed watching so much as it does at this moment," said Menelaos. "Did you happen to favor my wife with any of your conversation just before she left the house for Troy? I've often wondered what drove her away; Paris was never reason enough."

VI

"How good of you, Helen, to return my call so promptly," said Charitas. "I was broken-hearted that you weren't at home. Just as soon as I heard of your unexpected return, I went right over to your house. It seemed the least a girlhood friend should do. There's so much I want to hear. The other side of the garden is shaded—we'll go over."

"You've changed the garden, Charitas, I shouldn't have known it," said Helen. "It was lovely before, but you've improved it since I saw it last."

"Time does wonders," said Charitas. "Helen, your servant can wait outside with the sun-shade—you won't need it."

"She may stay with me," said Helen. "Adraste and I get on well together. Come here, Adraste, I want my old friend to see you—a friend of my girlhood."

"Oh, Helen, how beautiful she is! What an amazing person you are, to keep a beautiful girl like that in the house."

"I have no prejudice against beauty," said Helen— "why shouldn't I have Adraste with me?"

"Well, perhaps your husband isn't susceptible, and you haven't a son to worry you. My boy Damastor—you remember him? Oh, of course you don't; he was about to be born when you left for Egypt. Damastor is handsome as Apollo, and he loves everything beautiful. It's

terrible. I've tried to bring him up well. He's an artist,
I'm afraid—my father had a second cousin who was. I've
tried to keep his mind occupied, and there are not many
occasions in Sparta. There's Hermione, of course, and
I'd be ever so contented if he took a fancy to her. I've
interested him in gardening—most of this is his work.
But I don't think it will hold him long."

"You're afraid," said Helen, "that if he saw a beautiful girl he'd fall in love with her?"

"Well, you know what I mean," said Charitas.

"No, I don't," said Helen.

"I want him to be a credit to his bringing up, and fall
in love at the right time with the right girl," said
Charitas. "You and I know that beauty often leads to
entanglements with the inexperienced."

"It often leads to love, I believe," said Helen, "and in
the presence of great beauty all men seem to be inexperienced. There isn't enough of it, I suppose, to get
used to. You wish your boy to be respectable—fall in
love with a plain woman? Or entirely conventional—
marry one he doesn't love at all?"

"How cynical it has made you—I mean, you didn't
talk this way before you went away."

"Before I went away," said Helen, "we never mentioned the subject, your son not yet being born, but I dare
say I should have talked the same way then. I hope so.
It isn't cynical—it's merely honest. You know as well
as I that it's quite proper to marry some one you respect
but don't love. Society never will ostracize you for it.
And you know it's getting into the realm of romance when
you really lose your heart to your mate, even though he
or she isn't beautiful. That's more than respectable—it's

admirable. Something like that, I understand, you dream of for your boy."

"That doesn't quite cover my point of view," said Charitas.

"No, it doesn't quite cover mine, either," said Helen. "I ought to add that those two formulas, love without beauty and marriage without love, though they are respectable and conventional, are also very dangerous. Rare as beauty is, you can't always prevent it from coming your way, and if you see it you must love it."

"I don't know that you must," said Charitas; "some of us have previous obligations."

"If you've never given yourself to beauty," said Helen, "there are no previous obligations."

"Then you wouldn't try to stop a boy from falling in love with the first beautiful girl he sees?"

"I'd try to prevent him from falling in love with any other," said Helen, "and when the beautiful girl arrives it's his duty to love her. He probably will, anyway, whether or not he has contracted obligations with the respectable homely, and I'd rather have him free and sincere. The way you are going at it, Charitas, you will make your boy ashamed to love beauty, and he'll pursue it in some treacherous, cowardly fashion. Your ambition to keep him respectable may prevent him from being moral."

"Do you talk this way to Hermione?" said Charitas.

"I've had little opportunity to talk to her on any subject," said Helen, "but I should say the same thing to her. I hope she will love the most wonderful man she knows, and I'd like her to fall in love at sight, but in any case she probably will love as fate wills, and there's no use interfering. The ones that take advice are heart-free."

"Would you mind Adraste's waiting at the other end of the garden?" said Charitas. "There are one or two things I'd like to whisper to you."

"Adraste will wait at the end of the garden," said Helen. "But now she's gone, I must say, Charitas, I see no point in whispering. If it's unmentionable, don't let's say it."

"Helen, it's all very well for you to be frank, but perhaps you do harm to others. You oughtn't to say such things before the girl—and with reference to my son; you'll put ideas into her head."

"Dear Charitas, what possible ideas of ours are new to the young, who listen to nature? I mentioned your son only because you did, and I wished him a happy fate. You, it seems to me, gave him a bad character; you expressed distrust of him, and before the girl. She hasn't lost her heart to your description. You really ought to send him over to our house some day soon, to prove he's more of a man than you've tried to make him. I'm curious to see the boy."

"He's been there several times recently, to see Hermione," said Charitas. "I couldn't say it before your servant, but I'd be well satisfied if he cares for Hermione. No one could breathe a word against her."

"They probably could, in some circumstances," said Helen, "unless human nature is falling off. But I agree that she doesn't deserve it. Does she happen to be interested in Damastor? Her father always wanted her to marry her cousin Orestes."

"She never mentioned Orestes to me," said Charitas, "nor my son either, I must say. She wouldn't to his mother. She's been here quite often recently. Come to think of it, she's talked chiefly about—"

"Go on," said Helen, "about what?"

"Why, about you. She explained it all, and I must say she took a weight off my mind."

"You evidently expect me to understand you," said Helen, "but I'm quite in a daze. What did she explain? What was on your mind?"

"Oh, Helen, I really didn't mean to bring the subject up—not so soon. But now I might as well go on. She explained about you and Paris, and I was so thankful to know that you were the innocent party."

"Innocent of what? Are we speaking of crimes? A gratifying idea! Perhaps Hermione will explain it to her mother when I get home."

"Well, not crimes, if you prefer," said Charitas, "but I understood—we all did—that you ran away to Troy with Paris—that he was your lover, and you—you loved him. I confess I believed it, Helen—your husband made the same natural mistake. And since Paris was a prince, we thought he really was a gentleman. The moment Hermione explained his low character, and told me of the miraculous rescue heaven provided for you, I knew at once that you had been an unwilling victim, first and last. We're all so glad that Menelaos could see it too, and forgive you."

"Menelaos!" said Helen. "Well, to come back to Paris. Why does Hermione think his character was low?"

"He stole the furniture," said Charitas.

"What?" cried Helen.

"So I learned from Hermione," said Charitas, "and he forced you to go with him. Hermione expressed it very delicately, as a young girl should, but I got the idea that you resisted him all the way to Egypt, and there you were rescued. Really, Helen, it must have been a thrilling adventure."

"Charitas," said Helen, "I'm deeply interested in my daughter's version of my story. When did she tell you all this?"

"Most of it before you came home, some of it since. The other day she stopped in to say that since your return she had been able to confirm several details about Egypt."

"What about Egypt?" said Helen. "You mentioned the country when I came in this afternoon, and I didn't get the reference."

"Oh, Hermione gave me the names of the man and his wife with whom you stayed—Thon—Thonis? Is that it? and—Oh, yes, Polydamna."

"I stayed in Egypt with Thonis and Polydamna, did I?" said Helen.

"Didn't you?" said Charitas. "Hermione says you did."

"You'd better tell me all she said," replied Helen, "and then I'll correct anything she got wrong."

"It seems silly to be telling you, Helen—I'd rather have you tell me what happened. But you know, we thought you just ran away with Paris, until Hermione explained that he took you against your will, and robbed Menelaos of some things of value, and altogether showed himself for what he was. Then the wind blew you to Egypt instead of Troy—I'm sure it was the gods protecting you—and there you appealed for help, and Thonis would have killed Paris if he hadn't been in a sense a guest, entitled to sanctuary. But he made him go on to

Troy alone, and you and the stolen things remained with Thonis and Polydamna until your husband came for you and brought you home. That's true, isn't it?"

"Is it Hermione's idea," said Helen, "that there was no war about Troy?"

"Dear me, no—I mean yes," said Charitas, "the war was a deplorable but natural blunder, she says. Your husband and his friends went to Troy and demanded you back, and the Trojans said you weren't there. Of course our men wouldn't believe them. The Trojans said you were waiting for Menelaos to call for you in Egypt. That sounded terribly facetious, especially as they didn't deny that Paris had reached home. So there was nothing for it but to fight. Naturally, if you had been there, as Hermione says, the Trojans would have been glad to give you up."

"She says so, does she?" said Helen.

"Yes—to save the city; it stands to reason. But they could only defend themselves, once they were attacked, and when the city fell and the truth came out, it was too late. So much time lost! And nothing for Menelaos to do, after all, but go back to Egypt and bring you home. If I know your husband, Helen, he was irritated."

"He was," said Helen; "the voyage from Egypt was anything but agreeable. What else did Hermione say?"

"That's all, I think—"

"Charitas, have you told these stories to any of our friends?"

"To every one I could, Helen; I knew it would make them happy to have your reputation cleared—we're very fond of you."

"I see I shall be busy for some time," said Helen,

"correcting all this nonsense. I may as well begin with you now, Charitas. You really didn't believe Hermione?"

"Certainly I did! It was entirely plausible, and for your sake I wanted to believe it. I shouldn't have been much of a friend if I hadn't done my best."

"You thought it plausible," said Helen, "that Hermione should know the circumstances of my leaving home, when she was only a child at the time? For my sake you wished to believe I waited twenty years in Egypt because I couldn't come home without Menelaos' escort? Well, let me correct your error. Menelaos and I were blown down to Egypt on our way back. I never stayed with Thonis and Polydamna, though they are the people who sold us food and supplies. Paris and I made a very direct voyage to Troy; at least I enjoyed it and it didn't seem long. I loved him dearly. He never would have taken me away if I hadn't wanted to go. And he didn't steal the furniture. Some pieces did disappear, I understand, in the confusion, but they must be here somewhere in Sparta; Paris took nothing to Troy, and Thonis certainly gave nothing back to Menelaos on our trip home."

"Oh, Helen, don't tell me that; I've hoped for the best!" said Charitas. "I can't believe it as I look at you. You look so—you won't mind the word?—so innocent! And for you to contradict the creditable story yourself, and insist on being—on being what we thought at first! I can't make you out at all. And I can't understand now why you came home with Menelaos."

"Or why he came home with me," said Helen. "That is the queer part of it. All the relatives and friends are puzzled. I'm not going to suggest any explanation of his conduct. But he did want me to come back; he intended to kill me, but he changed his mind. If you want to go deeper than that into his motives, Charitas, ask him yourself sometime when he is over here. But I can give you at once my own explanation of myself. Thank you, dear Charitas, for saying I look innocent. I am innocent. That is, of everything except love. From what you said this afternoon, perhaps you think love is a crime. Let's compromise, and say it's a great misfortune—a misfortune one wouldn't have missed. There's every reason why we should be frank about our misfortunes, about our faults, too, for that matter, and certainly about the misery our faults and our misfortunes bring on others. Now if I allowed you to believe that shabby story about Egypt, I should be shirking the blame for all the wretchedness at Troy. I was there, and I was the cause of it all; to deny it would be to deny myself—to exist only in falsehood."

"For goodness' sake, Helen," said Charitas, "I'll go mad with your reasoning. You want the world to know you caused the wretchedness at Troy, and you want us to think you're as innocent as you look. What's your idea of innocence?"

"Charitas, I'm not easily provoked," said Helen, "but I've a mind at this moment to learn what is your idea of respectability. Here we are sitting in your garden, in broad daylight; your servants and perhaps the neighbors can see what disreputable company you keep. Shall I go now, or not until you've heard the rest of my story?"

"Don't be sensitive, Helen—finish the story. Of course I want to hear it. I hope for light."

"You won't get it from me," said Helen; "our experience hasn't been of the same order, and our ideas probably won't be. But here is my account of my innocence. I am used to having men fall in love with me, but I never wanted them to, and I never flirted with a man in my life. I simply existed; that was enough. And I never wished to love. To marry—yes; I was glad to marry Menelaos, but I had some of your prudent conviction that marriage is easier to arrange and carry through than love is. Against my will I fell in love with Paris. It just happened to me, and I don't consider myself responsible. But I could be sincere—that at least was in my choice, whatever else was fate. Since love had befallen me, I saw it through to the end. Charitas, sincerity was the one virtue I salvaged out of the madness, and I kept a little intelligence, too—I had enough wit to know that the end would be bad. I was deserting my child; what would happen to her character, growing up alone, and with such an example? When we reached Troy, the Trojans, I was sure, would repudiate Paris and me, else there would be war. But as it turned out, the Trojans did nothing of the sort. They welcomed me. When the war was going the wrong way for them, they said more than once that it was worth it, just to have me with them. Charitas, a woman who does a wrong she feels she can not help, yet expects to suffer for it, and is ready to pay the penalty as though it were altogether her fault—such a woman, in my opinion, is moral far above the average. By your own standards, I think—certainly by mine—the Trojans lost their sense of moral consequences. Hermione's story would save their reputations, but it does less than justice to mine. I am proud of my willingness to pay for what others suffered from my misfortune.

Without that moral clarity, I could have no peace of mind. And I think Menelaos, like the Trojans, showed that he was ethically confused. From the beginning of the siege, I could guess our people would win, and of course Menelaos would kill me. But instead he brought me home, as you see. Even the gods, it might be said, were delinquent, not to annihilate me—but perhaps I'm to suffer exquisitely now through my neglected daughter, who has grown up to have a respectable and dishonest imagination. Had I been here, I should have taught her to love the truth."

"Well, with the facts this way, Helen," said Charitas, "I can't understand Menelaos any more than I can you. I'd have sworn he'd be insane for revenge. He was always such a devoted husband."

"He was," said Helen, "he came for me with a knife or a sword or something. I hardly noticed; it made no difference to me. I expected it, and made no attempt to escape. I even made it easy for him, drew my robe away from my heart—so."

"Oh, it was then he decided not to kill you? Poor man! . . . Helen, you're impossible!"

"Why impossible, Charitas? Obvious and innocent, I think," said Helen. "Far more moral, I claim, than the world in which I have tried to lead a good life. If you had had my experience, and had grown used as I have to the odd turns things take, you'd either say that our ideas of justice have no basis in experience, or else that our misfortunes are the work of powers above us, who use us for their own purposes. Love, for instance. You'd better lift up your hands to it. It's terrible as well as beautiful. It isn't what you think it is, Charitas—it isn't just a word for a feeling we have."

"I haven't gone into the subject so deeply as you have," said Charitas. "No doubt you've talked this over many a time with Paris. You haven't said much about Paris."

"I loved him," said Helen, "and he is dead. What would you like me to say about him?"

"You don't mind my asking, do you?" said Charitas. "I wondered how he fitted into your philosophy. You loved him enough to run away with him, but now that he is dead you seem rather tranquil about it. Helen, it does make you seem hard-hearted; you ought to appear sad, anyway."

"If I tell you the truth, you'll not understand me," said Helen, "but the truth is, it wasn't Paris I loved; I loved something he made me think of. At first I thought I loved him—afterward I loved, and always shall, what I thought was Paris. First I loved him, then I was sorry for him."

"That's what I have against romance," said Charitas, "the disillusion afterward."

"Ah, you've heard of it?" asked Helen.

"Yes," said Charitas, "and in your case the disillusion must have made you feel it was an unusually bad mistake. That's why I can't see much in your philosophy of innocence, Helen."

"If that illusion was a bad mistake, Charitas, then most marriages are a fatal error. Please understand why I was sorry for Paris; I felt that he too was lost in a madness, lost for something not me, for something I made him dream of, something he would never find—lost as I was lost. But it happens in marriage too, if you begin with love. Many a good husband is a lost man.

When it comes to that, Charitas, how about the wives?
Isn't it my turn to ask how your own heart has weath-
ered the years?"

"I don't think I could speak of anything so intimate,
Helen, not even to you. Besides, I've nothing to tell.
My husband and I have been entirely faithful to each
other."

"But might not be," said Helen, "if there were a beautiful serving-girl in the house. As for yourself, Charitas,
do you mean you are still in the heyday of amorous illusion, or do you feel virtuous because you have always
managed to care for other men a little less, even, than you
have cared for your husband?"

"Don't talk that way, Helen; it hurts. I confess I'm
old-fashioned. I like the old ways of men and women."

"Adraste likes them, too," said Helen. "She seems to
have met a friend at the end of your garden. He's been
talking with her most confidentially, not to say affection-
ately, for the last fifteen minutes."

"Kind gods!" cried Charitas, "that's my boy Damastor! There, I told you, Helen, I told you!"

VII

HERMIONE was Helen's child, but Menelaos was her father. She had his dark hair, his black eyes, and his kind of regal bearing. She had the manner of knowing who she was. Helen was queenly by birth, Hermione by inheritance. She was not beautiful herself, but she called beauty to mind, and she had an admirable character. The world, she thought, might be set straight by intelligence and resolution. She was disposed to do her part. She stood before Helen now, tall and slender, much at ease, wondering why her mother had sent for her.

"Hermione, I find certain scandalous rumors circulating about me here in Sparta. Perhaps you can explain them."

"Which do you refer to, mother?"

"So you have heard of them. I must know their source, if possible, in order to stop them. Scandal is always annoying, and usually it is unnecessary."

"At times, mother, it is inevitable."

"Never," said Helen. "I've met people who thought so, but I don't take their view. In any case, the question hardly concerns us. I wish to get at the bottom of these stories in which I figure rather discreditably. When did they first come to your attention?"

"I'd rather forget than talk about them, mother."

"We'll dispose of them first and forget them afterward," said Helen. "Since there are several of these stories, which did you hear of first, and when?"

"There's a legend," said Hermione, "that you deserted your husband and ran away with Paris to Troy. I first heard of it right after you went."

"But that's not scandal," said Helen, "that's the truth."

"If that's not scandal, I don't know what it is."

"I see you don't," said her mother. "In scandal there's always some falsehood, something malicious and defamatory. Scandal, to my mind, is such a story as I heard yesterday afternoon from Charitas. She says I never was at Troy at all. Paris carried me off, against my will, and some valuable furniture too, for good measure. The winds blew us to Egypt—you know the absurd tale? Well, that's what I call scandal. What should I be doing in Egypt? And would I have gone off with Paris if he had been a thief?"

"The furniture was missing," said Hermione, "and you must admit, mother, Paris was the natural one to blame, since he—well, he did—what he did."

"What did he do?" asked Helen. "You were an infant at the time; I'd like to hear your account of the episode. Perhaps you supplied the malicious part of the scandal. Paris didn't steal me, as you were about to say, I was quite willing. But if he had stolen me, I'd prefer to think he would have had no margin of interest left for the furniture."

Hermione said nothing.

"Well?" said Helen.

"Mother, this is a terrible subject—I'd rather avoid it," said Hermione. "It isn't a subject for a girl to be talking to her mother about."

"What isn't?" said Helen.

"The character of the man who—who seduced you," said Hermione.

"Nobody seduced me, and I have not desired your opinion of Paris. You were a year old when he saw you last. What I want to know is something you may be able to tell me—how did these scandals begin?"

"If you insist on our coming to an understanding," said Hermione, "I think you oughtn't to turn the discussion from its natural path. I didn't want to say anything, but if we talk of it at all, it *is* a question of Paris. Of course when he left I had no opinion of him, but I have one now. I don't think highly of him. He's dead—and all that, but his conduct has seemed to me, still seems, shocking."

"My impression is that he couldn't help it," said Helen. "You'll admit I was in a better position to understand him. But that's not the point. How did such a story begin? Do you know?"

"Since you are determined to find out," said Hermione, "I made up all the stories myself."

"That's what I gathered from Charitas," said Helen. "I'm glad you have the frankness to own it. Oh, Hermione, how could you tell those lies? You needn't answer; it's the result of my leaving you—you had no bringing up."

"You hurt me," cried Hermione, "you hurt me with the hard things you say and the cool way you say them! I try to be dutiful, I call you mother, but we don't belong to each other. If you were human you'd know why I did what I could to save your name, to keep even a wild chance it might be a mistake, to support at least a

little good opinion for you to return to—if you came
back. Don't look at me so—you've no right to! If I had
a daughter telling me such truth as I'm telling you, I'd
feel shame—I couldn't be so shining and serene!"

Helen continued radiant and serene. "Respectability
based on falsehood," she said. "That's what your love
for me suggested. I've seen it tried before. Hermione,
you're very like your father. Like my sister, too, I'm
sorry to see. By the way, have you seen Orestes in my
absence?"

"From time to time," said Hermione—"that is, not
very often."

"What if you had?" asked Helen. "It wouldn't be a
crime, would it?"

Hermione said nothing.

"You needn't blush," said Helen, "it's not your
daughter speaks to you as yet; it's only your mother,
who embarrasses you with her liking for sincerity. As
a matter of fact, I've no doubt you've seen your cousin
frequently."

Hermione said nothing.

"There's nothing to be ashamed of, if you have," her
mother went on; "we once planned that you should
marry him, and I dare say he likes you. I raised the
question merely to examine your character a bit further.
You lacked courage about me, but I could excuse that—
you're young, and mine is an unusual case. But you
ought to have enough courage to tell the truth about
your own blameless life. You thought my reputation
would be improved by those extraordinary yarns; will
you tell me what your reputation can gain by lack of
frankness?"

"Orestes has been here often, I suppose," said Hermione, "but it doesn't seem often. Perhaps that's because I'm in love with him, as he is with me. I should have told you before, but I suspected you don't care for him."

"I don't care for him," said Helen, "but then I don't intend to marry him. Do you? You see the dilemma you've placed yourself in. If you wished to marry him, yet gave him up because I disapproved, I'd know you valued my opinion—and I'd know you weren't altogether in love. But if you are to marry him anyway, and defer to my opinion only by concealing your intentions, then I'm not flattered, and I foresee no happiness in your marriage. In marriage, if anywhere, you need the courage of your convictions, at least at the beginning."

"You hurt me so," cried Hermione, "I'm tempted to speak plainly enough to satisfy even you! I don't know whether it's the courage of my convictions, or just that I'm angry, but I don't admire your kind of courage, nor the kind of man you ran away with, nor your ideas about scandal! I still have some impulse—I don't know why I have it—to spare you the things you don't like but which can't be helped. I'm not so old as you, but I don't feel very young. I've grown up watching what you call your unusual career, and I realize without the slightest shame that I'm more old-fashioned than you are; I like the respectability you seem to dread, I want a lover I can settle down with and be true to, I'm going to have an orderly home. I'm sorry I tried to save your reputation for you, since you prefer it the other way, but no great harm was done,—none of your friends really believed me. What I did was out of duty, I have no reason to love you, I owe you gratitude for nothing. You never made me happy, you never made any one happy, not even those who loved you—not my father nor Paris, nor any of them. Paris must have seen—he was a fool to take you."

Hermione was a bit amazed, and on the whole gratified, at her own indignation and spirit. She felt it was a big moment. Helen too, strange to say, seemed pleased.

"Now you are telling truth," she said. "Thank heaven you are beginning, though it's at the bottom, where we so often begin—with unpleasant things about others. But I'd rather hear this than those silly fabrications of yours. Correct at every point; you have no reason to love me, and none to be grateful. As for Paris, I've often wondered why he loved me. For the same reason, I suspect, that your father didn't kill me, that night in Troy. I told Paris precisely what you have said—that I had made no one happy. I also told him that no man had made me happy—that what promised to be immortal ecstasy would prove but a moment, brief and elusive, that our passion would bring misery after it, that for him it would probably bring death. With his eyes open, and I can't say he was a fool, he chose our love. Or perhaps there was no choice. But surely your father knew the worst when he came to find me, sword in hand and murder in his heart. He had good right to kill me, and I thought he would. Or perhaps I didn't think so."

Hermione was put out that her mother wasn't angry. It seemed her turn to speak, but she couldn't get her wits together; she felt unexpectedly exhausted. She had been standing for some time; now she sat down on the couch beside her mother.

"Your facts are correct," Helen went on, "but some aspects of them you are too young to understand. I ought to have made you happy—one's child ought to be happy. But not one's lover; I deny any obligation there. If we only knew beforehand, and accepted the implications, that happiness is the last thing to ask of love! A divine realization of life, yes, an awakening to the world outside and to the soul within—but not happiness. Hermione, I wish I could teach you now that a man or a woman loved is simply the occasion of a dream. The stronger the love, as we say, the clearer and more life-like seems the vision. To make your lover altogether happy would be a contradiction of terms; if he's really your lover he will see in you far more than you are, but if you prove less than he sees, he will be unhappy."

"Don't you think you're a peculiar case?" said Hermione. "To you love may be this uncertain kind of trouble, but to other people, as far as I've observed them around here, it's a fairly normal, reliable happiness. At least they don't talk as you do, they look comfortable, and they congratulate the young who have agreed to marry."

"My dear child," said Helen, "I am a peculiar case—every one is who has known love. But there's some general wisdom about the matter which I'd share with you if I could. It's useless to try. You'll have to learn for yourself when you fall in love."

"I am in love," said Hermione,—"with Orestes."

"Yes, child, in love—but not very far in. I dare say he has never disappointed you, as yet."

"Never!"

"The early stage," said Helen. "We have to build up the illusion before we can be disappointed."

"I've a new light on scandal," said Hermione, "and I'll do my best to grasp your idea of love. May I ask you a personal question? I suppose this theory ought to apply to you as well as to the men who loved you. Has love for you too always been a mistake?"

"Never a mistake," said Helen, "always an illusion."

"So when you ran off with Paris, it wasn't really Paris you loved—as you found out later?"

"You might say that—it wasn't the real Paris."

"But you'll admit you hadn't the excuse you give me, of inexperience," said Hermione. "You had already loved my father, and I suppose had found out that he too wasn't what you wanted. You shouldn't have been deceived a second time."

"I married your father," said Helen; "I never said I loved him. But not to shock you and not to misrepresent myself, let me say I've always been fond of Menelaos, and he's an impeccable husband. Yet your argument would miss the point, even if I had been passionate over him. I should then have to confess the same disillusion in my love for Menelaos as in my love for Paris, but perhaps I preferred my illusion for Paris. It's the illusion you fall in love with. And no matter how often it occurs, no matter how wise you are as to what the end will be, one more illusion is welcome—for only while it lasts do we catch a vision of our best selves. In that sense, as I understand it, love is a disease, and incurable."

"Well, then," said Hermione, "when once a person has occasioned in you this divine vision of yourself, you might keep the happiness if you never saw the person again?"

"That's a profound insight," said Helen, "but to be so wise would be inhuman."

"One other question, mother—does father think as you do?"

"I doubt it, but you never can tell," said Helen. "Your father hasn't spoken to me at any length about his ideas of love—not for a long time."

"I'm sure he wouldn't agree with you," said Hermione, "and neither do I. Your praise of truth gives me courage to say I don't think all the people I know, except you, are wrong, nor that what seems their happiness is an illusion. For myself I want the kind of happiness I believe they really have. I shall never understand how you, so beautiful and so clever, with a husband you had chosen yourself from so many splendid suitors, could throw yourself away on that person from Asia. I've tried to imagine just what was your state of mind when you ran off with him, but I can't."

"No, in that direction," said Helen, "you failed rather notably. I come back to the scandal you spread. You told Charitas I went away because I couldn't help myself—Paris took me by force."

"It seemed the kindest version."

"Oh—was there a choice of versions? What have I escaped—which were the others?"

"Oh, what's the use, mother?" said Hermione. "I've owned up about the stories, and since you don't like them, I'm sorry. You only make me angry by the way you examine me. I tried to do right, but you make me feel cheap."

"If you were trying to do right, you have no cause to feel cheap," said Helen. "But I suspect you were uncomfortable even at the time; I credit you with too much intelligence to think you knew what you were talking about."

"I knew what I was about—I was telling a lie, for your sake, and also for the sake of the rest of us. I could have told more than one lie; I tried to choose the best. The first I thought of wouldn't do—I had it out of old-fashioned poetry—that situation you get so often where the gods deceive the lover by a spell, and he doesn't know who it is he takes in his arms, but afterward his eyes are cleared and he knows he's been tricked. I was so desperate at first, I thought of saying Aphrodite enchanted you, so you thought it was Menelaos, but it turned out to be Paris. Don't smile—I didn't waste much time on that threadbare poetry. Then I could have said you went with Paris willingly, but that was so obviously disreputable, and I couldn't explain it away. Besides, it was just what people were thinking. I saw it must be Paris taking you by force."

"Very strange, considering what I was telling you only a moment ago about love," said Helen, "but that first idea isn't threadbare poetry, and if you had told it I should never have called it scandal, for it's the truth. Paris couldn't have stolen me against my will. In a sense I went of my own accord. But in the deepest sense the story would have been true—it was the spell."

"Now really, mother, that's too much—not that—not at this late date!"

"Truth, Hermione, profound truth! You always think it's Menelaos you're embracing, and it turns out to be Paris."

"I give you my word, mother, never in my life have I heard a remark more cynical!"

"On the contrary," said Helen, "it's one of the most optimistic remarks you will ever hear, especially coming from me. You don't understand yet, and many who ought to know seem reluctant to tell, but in love there's always a natural enchantment of passion to draw us on, and when the enchantment dies as it must, there remains behind it either a disillusion, or a beautiful reality, a friendship, a comradeship, a harmony. This wonder behind the passing spell I've never yet found, but I have always sought it, and I persist in believing it may be there."

"If we all lived on your plan," said Hermione, "I don't see what would become of people. We haven't the right to lead our own lives—"

"If we don't lead our own life," said Helen, "we are in danger of trying to lead some one else's."

"I mean, we're not alone in the world," said Hermione. "You can talk me down, but I wonder you don't realize how queer your sense of proportion looks. You take me to task because I spread a story about you—false, I'll admit, but in the circumstances remarkably generous and favorable. Yet you have been preaching ideas here, with your quiet voice and those innocent eyes of yours, ideas which would make us all wicked if we followed them. Telling a little falsehood for a kind purpose doesn't seem to me so bad as destroying homes and bringing on war and taking men to their death."

"It wouldn't seem so bad," said Helen, "unless you asked what started the destroying of homes, the war and death. You might find that the remote cause was a little falsehood for a kind purpose. If we all lived on my plan, you said. I have no plan, except to be as sincere as possible. We certainly are not alone in the world, and the first condition of living well with the others, I think, is to be entirely truthful with them. How can anything be kind that is partly a lie? And you don't see what would become of people! Well, what's becoming of them now? Ever since I returned I've noticed how the kind ways of our fathers, the manners wise men agreed on for each other's happiness, can be turned to very mean uses. Charitas came over to see me at once. What could be kinder than to welcome an old friend home? Had she any honest business in my house if she didn't come as a friend? I've returned the call, and I know her through and through. She told me the legends you tried to circulate; of course she hoped they weren't true. She hoped for the worst. What she wanted when she rushed over here was the first bloom of the gossip, news of my most intimate experiences, to discuss my wickedness more specifically with the neighbors. And then, poor woman, she's never had any adventures herself. I disappointed her. She got no news, and made it clear that I am an entirely moral woman."

"Mother! How could you?" said Hermione.

"I won't go into the argument now," said Helen— "I'm growing tired of myself as a theme for conversation, and it's you I wanted to talk about. But I might leave this suggestion with you—that of all those who went to Troy on my account, I'm the only one who returned with an unimpaired sense of morality. If this talk has opened your eyes in the least degree, you may watch the people around you, and watch yourself, and you'll see what I mean. We have the right to lead our own lives—you've the right even to marry Orestes, though I still hope you won't. But that right implies another—to suffer the consequences. If I'd been home to train you properly, I shouldn't be telling you now that for intelligent people the time for repentance is in advance. Do your best, and if it's a mistake, hide nothing and be glad to suffer for it. That's morality. I don't observe much of it in this neighborhood."

"It's only fair to remember," said Hermione, "that Charitas has been a good friend to me in your absence. She'd be astonished if she knew what you think of her."

"She knows now, and she's astonished," said Helen. "I consider her a dangerous woman. Mark my words, she'll do a lot of harm. What sort of boy is that son of hers?"

"Damastor? Oh, well enough," said Hermione. "He hasn't his mother's steadiness of character, but he's harmless. He's devoted to Charitas."

"What do you mean by harmless?" asked Helen.

"Oh, he's well-behaved, sheltered and quiet, a bit young even for his years."

"You must admire his type," said Helen.

"What, Damastor?" cried Hermione.

"His mother says he's devoted to you."

"To me? I scarcely know him! Oh, I've seen him at his mother's, but not often. He's shown no signs of devotion, thank heaven! I've thought of him as a mere child."

"Then he hasn't been calling on you lately?"

"Never—who told you that?"

"Charitas. She says he told her. I thought myself it wasn't so. They're a very respectable family. No more than the normal amount of lying, I dare say. You might do worse."

PART TWO
THE YOUNGER GENERATION

THE YOUNGER GENERATION

I

"MENELAOS," said Helen, "may I have a word with you?"

"I'm busy. What do you want?"

"I want to talk with you about Hermione."

"Now, what's wrong with her?"

"Nothing's wrong. I just want to discuss her future. We haven't given it much thought yet, and you must feel as I do that we should plan together for the happiness of our child."

"That can wait," said Menelaos. "I'm crowded this morning. The thing isn't important, anyway; Hermione isn't unhappy."

"It's important to me, Menelaos. Hermione may not be unhappy—she isn't, I hope—but she has been much neglected. Now that we are home again we ought to study her, and provide the sort of life that will develop the best in her, and give her satisfaction as she grows older. I don't see how you can postpone the obligation a moment longer."

"Well, I like that!" said Menelaos. "If she has been neglected, kindly tell me who neglected her? You speak as though it were my fault!"

"We both of us left her, though for different reasons,"

said Helen. "I'll take the blame, if you like, but now we are here again, let us repair the harm. You share that ambition, I assume. For me, nothing is more important this morning; if you are too busy to put your mind on it now, will you set a time when we can talk? But you really aren't busy, Menelaos. When I came in you were standing there, gazing out the door."

"I wish you'd learn that a man may be profoundly occupied even standing still and gazing out a door. You don't half give me credit, Helen. If I didn't think hard and often, this place wouldn't hold together. It's perilously run down. I rather think I'm planning well for my child if I mend the property."

"You do manage well, Menelaos; no one appreciates it more than I. That's why I want to talk about Hermiore—it's your advice we need, before she commits herself too far."

"Commits herself to what?"

"Well, for one thing, to a husband."

"Oh—Orestes."

"That's one possibility, I suppose," said Helen. "She thinks she's in love with him."

"Fine!" said Menelaos. "Then that's settled. Was there anything else?"

"We haven't finished with Orestes yet," said Helen. "I don't think it's fine she imagines herself in love with him. I doubt if she knows what love is. She's determined to marry him."

"May I say 'fine' again—since you're asking my advice? Why shouldn't they marry? I thought we all agreed to that long ago."

"Exactly. Long ago. We've learned a good deal

since. What's experience for? Orestes is no husband for my child."

"Do you refer to our child? I like to be counted in, while my advice is being asked. As a matter of fact, I know what you're up to, Helen; you've made up your mind to do something or other, and you're breaking the news to me. I've had my advice asked before. Now please understand, once for all, that Orestes suits me, if Hermione wants him. And I haven't heard of any rivals. Come to think of it, you and I haven't seen him—since when? We shouldn't recognize him if we met. Hermione knows him much better than we do—they've been somewhat thrown together, I understand, by common interest in absent parents. What does she report of him?"

"She reports that she's in love with him. Nothing more specific. I certainly have no first-hand acquaintance with him, but I know his mother and you know his father—that's the politest way to put it; he must resemble one or the other."

"I can't say I ever liked your sister," said Menelaos, "but you ought to be more complimentary to Agamemnon, I should think; you often approve of his point of view—at least, you usually side with him against me, and he's uniformly civil to you. One of your admirers, in fact. But whatever you think of him and Clytemnestra, it seems unfair to lay the blame on Orestes."

"Blood will tell," said Helen. "I've always considered that the weak side of the house."

"Clytemnestra weak?" cried Menelaos. "Do you know your sister? Long ago I told Agamemnon he was a brave man to marry her. He'll believe me now, if ever he gets through with those bonfires of his and comes home. The night we parted I suggested that he wasn't eager to face his wife again. He'll remember the remark."

"What on earth do you mean?"

"Well, I didn't like to tell you before—she's your sister—it's one of the things I was thinking about when you came in. Eteoneus says Clytemnestra is through with Agamemnon—she has been living quite openly with Ægisthus, and she intends to have it out with my brother when he comes back. There'll be a dreadful dispute. I'm sorry for Ægisthus, whichever way it ends. If I knew just where Agamemnon is now—when you came in I was wondering how I could help him without hanging around Clytemnestra's door-step in an awkward way."

"She never did know how to treat a husband," said Helen, "and though I don't care for Agamemnon, I've always felt sympathy for him. Any man deserves a certain attitude on the part of his wife. If it's impossible for her, she ought to leave. But I don't see how Clytemnestra's behavior is an argument for marrying our daughter to her son."

"None at all," said Menelaos, "nor an argument against it. Don't condemn Orestes before we know him. Why not send for the boy and look him over? Or wait till he happens along—Eteoneus says he'll be here soon."

"How does he know that?"

"He doesn't really know it, but he says Orestes has been coming at regular intervals, and he may be expected shortly."

"So Eteoneus has been encouraging this affair when my back was turned?"

"You wouldn't think so, to hear him talk," said Menelaos. "He seems to like Orestes less than you do. They've quarreled—cursed each other like pickpockets, according to our gate-keeper, and I dare say he didn't tell me the worst. On the whole he supports your side of the question."

"Then he probably told you some sound reasons for not approving of Orestes. What does he say of him?"

"Since you press me," said Menelaos, "he fears that Orestes too much resembles you—in ideas, that is."

"That's his mother in him," said Helen. "Eteoneus never understood me. I'm sure the boy is Clytemnestra all over again; children usually take after the parent of the other sex."

"Nonsense!" said Menelaos. "You can't account for children so simply. Besides, that amounts to holding them responsible for their parents, and it isn't fair. As a matter of fact, they usually behave much more prudently."

"That's rarely a virtue on their part," said Helen. "It should be laid to their immaturity or to improper bringing-up."

"There you go!" exclaimed Menelaos. "Now the mad-house begins. How are you expecting to make a sane person believe that prudent behavior is the result of a bad education?"

"They shouldn't be prudent so young," said Helen, "it's a bad sign. It's beginning at the wrong end. Youth should begin by loving life. Prudence is a form of caution, it's a control of your impulses—but you must have the impulses before you can control them. Or it's a kind of foresight—but how can you have foresight until you have accumulated some knowledge of the world? And how can you accumulate experience if you begin by avoiding it? When they're young they can have nothing better in them than the love of life. Now, that's just what they haven't, and their prudence is therefore an empty thing, in my opinion."

"From what I've heard of the young people," said Menelaos, "they've about all the love of life we can stand. Eteoneus thinks so of Hermione and Orestes, and I dare say he's right."

"Since when have you gone to your gate-keeper for your philosophy, Menelaos? Eteoneus is a faithful drudge, I have always thought—and a very ignorant man. He knows as much of life as one can contemplate from a door-mat. I feel you are trifling with me. Won't you be serious?"

"I am serious. I can be more so, if you really wish it. But before we begin, may I say I didn't go to Eteoneus for anything—he came to me. He sometimes leaves the door-mat to seek a moment of my society, and though he's not the companion of my choice, he's far from a fool. But seriously—as you put it—since you won't leave me in peace, what's all this about Hermione's bad up-bringing, and the love of life she hasn't got, and the husband she ought to have? I'm distracted this morning, Helen, over the news of Agamemnon, and other matters seem less important than perhaps they are. What do you want?"

"I want your attention," said Helen, "and if I can't have it now, I'll wait. But Hermione is in a danger, I think, from which we could save her if we planned quickly, and since I fear she got into this peril through my leaving her, I'll run no risk of not saving her now. If we don't prevent it, she'll marry Orestes, and that marriage, I'm sure, will bring her nothing but misery. She's seen no other man of her age but Orestes and Damastor—you know, the Charitas boy, and he's not much. By contrast Orestes must seem a god. It's usually by contrast. Some day she'll meet a real man, and be sorry she married prematurely."

"Upon my word!" said Menelaos. "Upon—my—word!"

"What she needs is experience—experience," Helen went on, "and as quickly as possible!"

"Oh, that's what she needs, is it?" said Menelaos. "Well, perhaps I can arrange for some one to elope with her without marrying her, and after a while she'll be able to pick the kind of husband she won't want to run away from. Let's consider it settled. Have you any one in mind for the trial flight?"

"You're not serious now, of course," said Helen. "But do you know, that wouldn't be a bad idea, if it could be carried out. It can't, I suppose, and it does go rather beyond what I thought of. Besides, it wouldn't do any good, she wouldn't learn anything, unless there were somebody she wanted to elope with, and I don't think there is."

"On the whole, isn't that a weight off your mind?" said Menelaos. "The way you talked, I thought she was eloping this afternoon. My own idea of Hermione is that she's steady and sensible and trustworthy. She's a great comfort to me. Why don't you let her live her life, as you've lived yours?"

"Menelaos, can't you, can't you see? That's precisely

what I want for her, but it's what she'll never do. If Hermione had my temperament, I shouldn't worry about her; I'd be sure she would live her own life, as you say, and whether or not she made mistakes, she wouldn't miss anything. But she's full of convictions and prejudices— what the world expects of her, as though the world cared—what she owes to herself, as though life were collecting a debt—and how much does she know about the world, or about herself? All her ideas are shallow and sentimental, purely formal; she has picked a scheme of things out of this little neighborhood, and she thinks she knows the universe. Poor child! Her heart is asleep. When she wakes up some day she may be terrible. Clytemnestra as a girl was just that way—positive, silly and sentimental. She married Agamemnon largely because you married me; the double alliance seemed to her romantic. I'm sure Hermione thinks there's something touching and pretty in marrying her cousin and keeping the family together. I don't call her prudent—she is blind. If she weren't so like her aunt, I shouldn't worry. A girl without any latent force of character might as well marry now as she wishes, find out her mistake at leisure, and take refuge in a comfortable, self-stifling career, like Charitas; the world's full of them, and at least they're safe. But if I know my child she'll find out her mistake by discovering a great passion, and she won't know what to do with it—she'll simply be violent. It's bad for that type when the love of life gets hold of them and they think it's too late."

"I'm not sure I understand what the love of life is," said Menelaos. "It's a phrase you often use, and like other phrases of yours it has a critical edge which seems to cut my way. I fancy you refer to something you think is lacking in me. Yet I really believe I love life as much as I ought to; I've never wanted to die. I've loved my people, and my home. I've loved you, Helen, in my poor way, for some time. I'm very fond of Hermione. Is there anything I've overlooked?"

"In your own way you have loved me, I think," said Helen. "We'll agree it's more than I deserved. But I don't thank you for it, Menelaos. Love is something that happens to us, we can't help ourselves, and the real passion isn't a compliment or a gift, and it isn't a sign of generosity in the lover. Your kindness and your patience when you haven't understood me—that's what I can thank you for. We're not farther apart than most husbands and wives, I dare say, and when we get to the end of our days we'll remember chiefly how long we have been companions. But, oh, Menelaos, I wanted Hermione to know the real thing! To have the passion and the heart-ache when she is young, when her body and her mind are undulled, when the ecstasy is in the senses and yet seems to be in the soul! And then, when the body flags and grows old, to find the ecstasy indeed in the spirit after all, their two souls melted in that fiery happiness! Or if she missed that joy, at least to come so near it that she'd know it could be, and she'd always think of it with yearning and measure life by it. It must happen to some people, Menelaos, and I wanted it for her. Those who have it never grow old, I think, never lose courage, nor lose interest; they may suffer, but their world remains beautiful. They can let their heart go—it won't be chilled or dwarfed or warped."

"You are frank," said Menelaos. "I'm glad you told

me—I suppose I'm glad. I suspect it's not the younger generation you are talking of. Well! So that's what you mean by love of life?"

"No, that is love," said Helen.

"Since we're on the subject, I might as well hear the rest of it," said Menelaos. "Can you give me a brief definition of whatever it is the young people lack?"

"I meant simply, they don't love life as they should," said Helen. "We usually pretend they do, because it would seem natural to delight in the world before us when we are young. But they take it very cautiously and seriously; haven't you noticed they see its faults first of all, and are highly critical? Love of life doesn't just happen to us, like that other love—I suppose it's an art, to be learned by practise, over a great deal of time. When we have learned it at last, we have probably ceased to be young. Perhaps these children can't be expected to love what they know so little about. They are afraid of life, afraid they won't succeed, or won't get married, or something. When their fears are removed they are so relieved that they settle down and never take a risk again. That's the only way I can explain most of the people I've met."

"But why do you explain Hermione that way? So far as I can see she'll love life if she gets a chance; till now, you'll admit, she's had more to worry about than young folks ought to have. Even at that, though I don't pretend to be a judge of these things, I've thought she was getting on pretty well. If she isn't, probably Orestes will teach her—I understand he's an enterprising young man, with the modern ideas."

"Oh, Menelaos, you don't get the point at all! Orestes

is incurably serious and dangerously resolute, with no experience, with no gift for living, with absolutely no sense of humor. Every one says that of him. Perhaps you think it a favorable report. He's the kind of young person who sees the flaws in life before he sees life, and is too conscientious not to remedy at once every flaw he sees. He will do his duty at any cost to others; he'll carry out what he thinks is the will of heaven even if he has to kill somebody. Of course he would commit the murder with the finest feelings, very reluctantly. I know that type. He's not the man to teach Hermione—he's unteachable himself. Can't you imagine what a wretched time he's going to have—and any woman who marries him? Menelaos, do help me to save Hermione!"

"Too bad we can't point to a shining example in the neighborhood for her guidance—unless she could be persuaded to copy your career."

"No, I don't want her to copy my career," said Helen. "I want her to have a far more brilliant one, a happier one, with more love in it. She doesn't admire me, and I don't blame her. I wish she had more of Adraste's temperament. There's a child who has the love of life. I've trained her carefully."

"God help her!" said Menelaos. "From my point of view she's more likely than Hermione to get into trouble."

"I should say the danger is about equal, though for different reasons. That silly Charitas boy is besieging her, and in a nasty sly way. He tells his mother it's Hermione he's in love with. I fear Adraste imagines there's more to him than there is."

"Every once in so often," said Menelaos, "your vein of thought escapes me entirely. You don't want Hermione to fall in love, because she hasn't the love of life. You don't want Adraste to fall in love, because she has. Isn't anybody to fall in love?"

"For a woman," said Helen, "falling in love means falling in love with a man. As usual, you overlook the central part of the problem. Certainly I don't want either of these girls to give herself to an unpromising man. Orestes and Damastor are not much alike, except that they are both impossible. Orestes has no love of life— Adraste would see through him in a minute. Damastor pretends to have a love of life, but at bottom he's the coward his mother has made him. I hope Adraste will find him out in time. I wish Pyrrhus were here."

"Pyrrhus—Achilles' son?"

"Yes."

"What do you want with Pyrrhus?"

"I'd like him for a son-in-law," said Helen.

"Now the cat's out of the bag!" said Menelaos. "But would Hermione like him for a husband? I suppose we'll leave her some privilege of choice? She's a grown woman, and she never saw Pyrrhus in her life."

"Ah, but there's always a danger she may see him, any time. Better to see him now, before it's too late. He has it in him—all I've been speaking of, and when Hermione sees him, she'll recognize it without being told. Unless she's past saving, she'll lose her heart to him."

"I've seen him often," said Menelaos, "and I didn't lose my heart. There's nothing miraculous about Pyrrhus."

"Oh, there isn't?" said Helen. "I really thought there was. I understood that you and Agamemnon had to ask his help after his father died. Perhaps there was nothing miraculous about Achilles, either. We needn't argue about terms. Pyrrhus is the kind of miracle I want for Hermione. When I think of a passionate excellence, of a soul alive, I think of that young man. For a good reason, too—he was the child of a great love."

"A love-child, you mean," said Menelaos. "Something shady, as you'd expect of Achilles. His birth was a scandal."

"It was not!"

"It certainly was!"

"It certainly wasn't!"

"Oh, very well! I dare say it looks quite edifying to you. He masqueraded as a girl, and so got into Lycomedes' house, to be a companion to the old man's daughters. One of them soon found herself the mother of Pyrrhus. By all means, let's introduce him to Hermione as soon as we can!"

"You're not fair, Menelaos! It was his own mother who tried to bring up Achilles as a girl, because she knew he would die in battle, and she hoped desperately to cheat fate. I don't admire her strategy, but any one could understand it. Achilles didn't masquerade a moment after he was old enough to realize the trick. He never did a sly thing. Deidamia wasn't deceived or betrayed!"

"She certainly wasn't," said Menelaos, "but her parents were. Those two famous young people were a nasty lot."

"You have a base heart to say so—you know better!" said Helen. "They grew up boy and girl together, closer in their childhood than brother and sister; when the time for love came, and the mystery enveloped them, they drew into each other's arms as beautifully as their hearts and their dreams had already drawn together. Achilles loved her till he died. He left her only because you asked him to fight for you and Agamemnon. He left her with her father Lycomedes, who held him always in honor. She taught the little boy to revere his absent father as a god, Achilles lived on news of his child. I don't see the trail of shame there. I see rather the heroic youth who chose to live a short time gloriously, rather than last out the usual prudent and meaningless years. I see the lover who, really knowing his mate, took her, and was utterly happy himself, as he made her to be. If the child they begot isn't a miracle, he's nearly so—their love was miraculously perfect."

"It's my turn to say something now. Talk all you want about the love of life," said Menelaos, "and define it so as to prove I haven't any. But when it comes to Achilles, I knew him a lot better than you did. At least, that's my conviction. I've never believed the story the army used to whisper, that you and he met in secret during the siege."

"I never met him in my life," said Helen.

"I'm sure you didn't," said Menelaos.

"But I would have met him if it had been possible," said Helen.

"I'm sure of that too," said Menelaos. "But if you had known him you wouldn't praise him so extravagantly. Achilles was a legend. He bolstered up the army, and in that sense was necessary, but only for the psychological effect. The Achilles you think you know was a myth. Loved Deidamia all his life, did he? Why, our whole quarrel was over that woman of his, Briseis!"

"To be sure—or you might say it was over Agamemnon's woman, Chryseis," said Helen. "The quarrel was over the spoils, and women figured in it, but neither was in love with his captive. You know very well Achilles, at least, had nothing to do with Briseis. His honor, not his heart, was offended when your brother took her away. She loved Achilles, of course—that was inevitable."

"We're not likely to agree," said Menelaos, "and it's ancient history now. In any case, even if Achilles had all the virtues, why the enthusiasm over Pyrrhus? You can't marry Hermione to Achilles, and very probably Pyrrhus will resist your kind intention to wish her on him. He may not like us any more than I like his family. Before you pin too many hopes to him, you should consider that he isn't his father."

"I consider that he's the next best," said Helen. "With experience perhaps he'll be even more remarkable. He showed the same high spirit when Odysseus came to fetch him for you, and his mother wouldn't let him go, to die like his father. You remember how the boy insisted on his right to live out his fate, thinking that to be safe in those circumstances, when you needed him, was to be disgraced. His old grandfather was proud enough of him, and sent him off with a blessing. You'll not deny that he finished the war for you, and went home with a great reputation. If he didn't earn it, how did he get it? If you and Agamemnon hadn't thought well of what he did, you wouldn't have given him, among his other prizes, Andromache, Hector's wife. I want Hermione to know Pyrrhus. At least to talk with such a man, to meet him familiarly around the house for a few days, and see for herself. After that, let her make her choice. You're quite right—he may not care for her, but after his visit she won't be so ignorant. Ask Pyrrhus to come here, Menelaos—do ask him to come at once!"

"I see myself!" said Menelaos. "He and I don't sleep under the same roof!"

"Why not, pray?"

"I won't have him in the house, that's why not. I wonder I put up with you, you—you—! I can't excuse myself for listening to your impudence—telling me—*you* telling *me*—what your blessed ideas are of a satisfactory love and a happy home! So far your good looks have got you out of what you deserved—may the gods forgive themselves for that!—but it won't be your fault if you don't go too far, even yet. You haven't the first instincts of a decent woman! You took me in at the beginning—this morning, I mean—with your solicitude for your child's future. Much you care for your child's future! Sooner or later you give yourself away—it's your love affairs, not Hermione's, we're to plan for! Any man, old or young, mean or noble, any at all, when the mood comes on you to make a fool of him! You loved Achilles, and still do, dead or alive, so I'm to invite his son here as the next best! For Hermione to see! Great chance she'd have to see him! Paris—Hector—Achilles—I won't mention the years, but can't you consider you've had your day? And quite a day! Measure in all things; do confine your disgrace to one generation!"

"Menelaos," said Helen, "your bad manners when you lose your temper are nothing new, but I had no idea you were so jealous. Jealousy is the one form of insanity which is dishonest. It begins in a wilful perversion of the facts. If I had ever given you any cause for jealousy, and if you had ever thought well of me, you would have grieved over your generous but unintelligent mistake; you wouldn't have cursed me for being myself, therefore sufficiently cursed already. If you thought me in love with Pyrrhus, you wouldn't be content to live with me, you wouldn't be at peace, just to know that Pyrrhus was out of my reach; you couldn't bear to live with me, if you thought me what you just said. You reminded me of our years. It's too late, therefore, to improve your manners. But I detest lying, at any age. Try to be honest with yourself, Menelaos, and try to be as frank with me as I am with you. I will take no insults from you—and you may understand that nothing true is to me insulting. The details of my life are well known—largely through my own efforts to disguise nothing. Your career, I regret to say, is more obscure. But for this once we are going to understand each other completely and equally. Do you wish me to stay here as your wife, honored and respected? There's no question of other men for the moment—this is between you and me. Do you want me? Or do you wish to kill me? If you really have no use for me, I won't stay a day longer. If you'd feel better to kill me, I'll gladly go bring you your heroic sword. You left it in the dining-room, I think. But it's one or the other. Which do you want?"

"I merely said I wouldn't have Pyrrhus—"

"Which do you want, Menelaos?"

"Which what?"

"It's no use, Menelaos, you'll have to answer me. I left this house once, and I can do it again. If I leave it this time at your own request, you can't bring me back. I'll stay on the one condition, that you insult me no more. Do you wish me to stay?"

"The question is rather complex," said Menelaos. "May I think it over?"

"It is complex," said Helen, "but it will be worse if you think it over. It's best to make one simple decision and be done with it."

"If you go now," said Menelaos.

"Or if you kill me," said Helen.

"It would be very difficult," said Menelaos, "to explain it to people. It would seem to indicate a certain indecision."

"Oh, you could explain it easily enough," said Helen. "Tell them the truth. Truth conquers all things—or is it love? Truth to be equally impressive. Tell them that I loved Paris and ran off with him—deserted you—spent years in his arms—and you forgave me and took me back. Then tell them that afterward you knew I admired Achilles, who was dead, and whom I had never seen—so of course you had to put me out or kill me, to take the stain off your honor. They'll understand you."

"I doubt if they will," said Menelaos. "Paris would, or any one else who had intimate experience of your gift for putting a man in the wrong, but most people, I dare say, will always think you're as easy to live with as you look. I'd rather put the question to you. Stay if you like, or go. If you stay, and if you won't irritate me too much, I'll try not to say what I think."

"That won't do," said Helen, "you mustn't think it."

"I'll try," said Menelaos, "I can't do more."

"I don't want any more," said Helen. "I've learned to be reasonable. Now let me be quite clear about the other men. I loved Paris. That's always been understood. I respected—even revered—Hector, but I couldn't love him. He was the finest example I shall ever meet of a temperament I don't like. He wasn't a joyous person—wasn't even before the war. That love of life we were talking of—he hadn't a bit of it. Anything gloomy looked to him like duty. He worried over any trouble he escaped. Of course he enjoyed life more than he liked to confess. He'd say that war was tragic, and no good would come of it, and in the same breath he'd pray that his little boy might grow up to be a more famous fighter than himself. As for Achilles—don't get excited now— if I had known him, I'm sure I should have loved him, him only, forever. We must love the best—there's no sin in love like failing to love the best—and he was the greatest of you all. Had he been one of my suitors, and had I known enough of life then, I should have taken him. It's not your fault nor mine, and you will be just enough to admit that I think of him only what the world thinks. I hope you will do me the justice also to recognize that I want his son, not for myself, but for my daughter."

"Will you do me the justice," said Menelaos, "to remember that I too may have ideas of life and love? That I too, though less remarkable than Achilles and you, have a part in the world, important at least to me? When people marry, and one of them is exceptionally brilliant, it's enough to ask of the obscure husband that he be proud of his wife, helpful to her career, and loyally keep in the background. He deserves some reward, I think."

"He does," said Helen, "and he's practically certain to get the reward he deserves. He'll lose his wife. Poor thing, she thought she was marrying a man, a great man, some one to be her mate, not her slave. She probably has exaggerated his merits, as he has hers, but she'll make

believe he has them, as long as she can. When he begins
to insist that he's nobody, in comparison with her, it's
all over."

"What is?" said Menelaos.

"Their life together," said Helen.

"But suppose, speaking in the abstract," said Menelaos, "suppose the deserted husband went after her and
brought her back; that would be an improvement,
wouldn't it? She'd begin to think more of him, wouldn't
she?"

"In the abstract, yes," said Helen— "especially if he
were able to manage it all single-handed."

"My word!" said Menelaos.

"And you'll ask Pyrrhus to come at once?" said Helen.

"Not at once nor later!" said Menelaos.

"It's at once we need him," said Helen.

"He'll never set foot in my house!" said Menelaos.

"The details can be arranged at any time," said Helen.
"The important thing is to get him here soon."

II

"HERMIONE, my child, come here," said Menelaos. "I must ask you a question. Sit down. Have you the love of life?"

"What's that?" said Hermione.

"Don't ask me hard questions—answer mine," said her father. "Do you love life?"

"Oh, yes indeed!" said Hermione.

"Very well, then, do you love it enough?"

"How should I know? What is enough?"

"We will now apply the test," said Menelaos. "Do you earnestly desire to marry Orestes?"

"Yes, I do," said Hermione.

"That answers it. You haven't the love of life."

"I don't see how that proves it," said Hermione.

"Nor I," said Menelaos, "but it proves it to your mother, who knows more than we do about such matters. I hope you will conduct yourself accordingly."

"Father, I wish you wouldn't tease me about what I consider—any one would consider—a serious thing!"

"Just to what do you refer?" said Menelaos.

"To marriage, of course!"

"That is serious," said her father, "but I hadn't got to that yet. I was finding out whether you had the love of life, because if you have it, you may marry any time, even if it's the wrong man, but if you haven't, you must postpone the wedding, even if it's the right one."

83

"I wish you'd tell me what you are talking about,"
said Hermione.

"All in good season," said Menelaos. "I must first
ask you another question or two. Is there any one you
would like to elope with?"

"I don't want to elope! I want to marry Orestes."

"Hasty again," said Menelaos. "You should elope
first. Your mother says you should, though she fears
you won't."

"My mother wants me to elope?" said Hermione.
"Why?"

"I believe the idea is that sooner or later one elopes,
and your mother, having tried it later, thinks it had better
be sooner. Enough of that. Would you like to see Pyrrhus for a few days?"

"Who's Pyrrhus?"

"You know—Achilles' son."

"Why should I want to see him for a few days?"

"It would be good for you—for your acquaintance
with the world at large. Pyrrhus is the cure for your
sheltered life. If our high opinion of you is justified,
you would fall in love with him."

"I'm already in love with Orestes, father!"

"Then you might elope with Pyrrhus, discover your
mistake, and marry Orestes afterward."

"I don't think this is funny," said Hermione. "I'm
rather hurt. May I go?"

"No, daughter, you mayn't. Come back here and sit
down again. Help me to collect my wits. I've been talking with your mother about you and Orestes, and I'm
rather done up. She's worried for fear he isn't the right
one for you, after all, and I dare say we ought to think

the matter over. Your mother's ideas she'll probably lay before you herself; I've merely sketched them in outline. For myself, I approve of Orestes, and you and I understand each other well enough to discuss him without reserve, and I hope, without excitement. Tell me what sort of a man he's grown to be."

"He's rather tall—really very good-looking," said Hermione, "and he has a winning personality. I don't think it's my partiality—I'm sure you'll like him."

"Of course," said Menelaos. "Skip his charms and come to his virtues. What sort of temperament has he—character, and all that?"

"He's very thoughtful," said Hermione, " if anything, a bit too serious, but it's what you'd call a good fault. He's much more introspective than you'd expect a young man to be, and he has a profound sense of duty. I feel quite frivolous when I'm with him. He's much too good for me."

"I doubt that last," said Menelaos. "See here, Hermione, that account of him is all very well for me, but don't give it to your mother. You'd better describe his wilder side when you talk to her—his faults. What are some of his worst?"

"He hasn't—well, I won't say he hasn't any, since every human being has some, but he's so kind and considerate of me, so devoted to his parents, so careful to guard my reputation and his own, that I don't see where you could find a bad fault in him."

"He's clearly a remarkable youth," said Menelaos, "but I can tell you now, your mother will never approve of him. You must choose eventually between your mother and Orestes."

"I choose Orestes now," said Hermione.

"I'll stand by you," said Menelaos, "but I'm not sure your mother won't have her way. Did I understand that he's devoted to his parents?"

"He worships his father," said Hermione.

"How does he feel about his mother?"

"You've heard about it, then," said Hermione. "I didn't know the story had got around, and I preferred not to be the first to tell it. Of course he grieves over his mother's conduct, but she is his mother, after all, and Agamemnon hasn't treated her any too well. Orestes is terribly unhappy. I've advised him at every stage—he has no one else to consult."

"What's the matter with his sister—what's her name—Electra?" asked Menelaos.

"He can't see her," said Hermione. "She's at home, in a very dangerous position, hoping to warn her father, or help him, when he gets back. She hurried Orestes out of the way as soon as Ægisthus became the head of the house; she said Ægisthus wouldn't let him grow up to take revenge. That's why he's leading such an unsettled life; he's hiding, yet watching for the moment his father will return and need him."

"How long has all this been going on, Hermione?"

"Oh, several years. Just when Clytemnestra began to care for Ægisthus, nobody knows, of course, but they've been talked of for a long time, and about three years ago, I should say, she introduced him to every one as her true husband. That's when he openly took possession of Agamemnon's property, and Electra got Orestes safely out of the way. He came and asked me what to do. Our old gate-keeper wouldn't let him in."

"I understand that the visit, and other visits, took place, nevertheless," said Menelaos. "Eteoneus regrets the unpleasantness. But I ought to tell you, if you don't know it, that Orestes didn't make a good impression on the gate-keeper. In fact, your cousin isn't popular here. How do you explain it? You don't want to marry a man who can't get on with people. When your mother criticized him I stood up for him, naturally; she's no judge of men. But I had in mind all the while the opinion of Eteoneus, and the old fellow is rather shrewd. Understand me, Hermione, I'm not against Orestes, but you ought to look into the thing from every angle."

"The trouble with Eteoneus, father, is his age. He thinks he can settle the affairs of the universe, and he has seen no more of the world than has come through your door. He lives on gossip—he was whispering about Clytemnestra before Orestes told me a word about it, and he's always stirring up the servants. How can he take the point of view of young folks brought up as Orestes and I have been?"

"I wish you would tell me how you've been brought up," said Menelaos; "it might perhaps reassure your mother."

"I mean, we've been thrown on our own resources, and we know our own minds. It's too late in the day to lead us by the hand. Our elders have made a mess of things; we're the true conservatives. How could Eteoneus, with his head full of etiquette, lighten the burden Orestes is carrying?"

"There's something in that," said Menelaos, "but you haven't answered the whole question. Even if we grant that Orestes is in trouble not of his making, and that he

knows his own mind, he still may be the wrong husband
for you. How's it all going to come out? How am I to
arrange the wedding for you? I can't have anything to
do with Ægisthus, and I wouldn't be caught in the same
town with Clytemnestra. We'll have to wait till Agamemnon comes home and puts his house in order; then
we can see what's left. In the meantime, hadn't you
better postpone making up your mind about Orestes?
Oh, yes, I know, you're in love with him—no objection to
that—but don't do anything hasty. I don't let Helen's
prejudices influence me, but the more I think of Orestes,
the more I wish he belonged to another family. You
must be happy, if your mother and I can assure it. And
I'll confess I'd like to recover thoroughly before we take
on another quarrel."

"See here, father, how did you and mother come to
have this obsession about marrying me off? In the five
years before you two got back, I hadn't thought so much
about marriage as you've made me think in the last few
days. My mind was on you and her, and on your troubles, and I was concerned for the family reputation; I
had Orestes and his problems to worry over, and what
sort of advice I ought to give him. Really, I haven't
thought of myself at all. In a general way I knew I
should marry Orestes, sometime in the future, when all
these other things were completely straightened out;
meanwhile he was my best friend, my one companion.
We are made for each other, I believe. When mother
asked me if I loved him, I said yes, and I told her I expected to marry him. It made me feel rather brazen to
say it right out, but she was insistent. I felt in my bones
she wouldn't approve of him; of course he entirely dis-

approves of her. But I certainly was taken back when she scolded me for not telling her more bluntly what my plans were. Have you heard her talk on the virtue of being perfectly frank? But I must say, father, you are now almost as difficult as she; you ask me whether I have the love of life, and other facetious questions, and then you abruptly turn serious and advise me to think it over and not marry Orestes in haste. What made you think I was going to marry him in haste? Won't you tell me frankly, as mother would say, what you really want of me? Don't you wish me to marry any one at all? Very well, I won't, if you need me at home. I dare say Orestes won't be free to think of matrimony for some time. Or are you hard on Orestes just because his parents aren't happy together? I naturally can't see any justice in that reasoning."

"To tell you the truth," said Menelaos, "I hadn't thought much myself about your marrying—perhaps not nearly enough—until Helen talked to me about it; we expected you to marry Orestes sooner or later, but meanwhile I was glad of you here—your being in the house makes it very pleasant for me. On the other hand, I dare say you are old enough to have a home of your own and lead your own life; it's too easy for your mother and me to forget where the years have gone, and to think you still a child. So I certainly do want you to marry. I haven't a thing against Orestes—nothing whatever, and strictly speaking I don't blame him for his parents. But Clytemnestra does spoil it all for me, I must say. I wish you could find a safe young man whose mother isn't too good-looking."

"It's no use, father, I simply won't marry Damastor!"

"Well, who wants you to?"

"Mother suggested it, and I gather from your last words that you agree."

"Your mother wants you to marry Damastor?"

"Now, I won't say that, father—she suggested him, and said I might do worse, but I doubt if she likes him, and I thought her tone rather satiric. I don't know mother well enough to get all her meanings."

"I don't either," said Menelaos, "but of one meaning I'm sure—it isn't Damastor she means you to marry!"

"Who, then?"

"She'll tell you in her own way. Remember to be completely surprised when she comes out with it. But just to provide against a shock, I'll drop the hint now— she intends to marry you to Pyrrhus."

"But I don't know the man! I don't want him! He probably doesn't want me!"

"It's curious," said Menelaos, "but those very ideas occurred to me when she proposed it."

"Then why does she persist in so crazy a scheme?"

"Better ask why she schemes at all," said Menelaos. "I rather think your mother is getting old. She doesn't look it, I'll admit, but she's in her forties and she's been through a great deal. All this talk about the love of life's a bad sign. The same way with this match-making. You'd think marriage would be an exhausted adventure for her. It is; that's why she begins to arrange marriages for others. When we are through playing leading parts ourselves, we try to play God and control the new actors. It's a gesture of farewell."

"Is Pyrrhus good-looking?" asked Hermione.

"Very," said Menelaos.

"I wouldn't be too sure about the gesture of farewell," said Hermione. "If mother happened to like him, I should say her youth is not beyond recovery."

"You've thought of that too?"

"What too, father?"

"I mean, you think she may be in love with Pyrrhus?"

"Oh, I know only what you've told me, but I don't agree that mother is growing old. Quite the reverse. She's so—what shall I call it?—she's so vital, she makes me feel, after a talk with her, as though I had been keeping up with some one who had wings."

"I won't have Pyrrhus here, that's all there is to it," said Menelaos. "Later it may be safe, but as you say—"

"That's not what I meant, exactly," said Hermione. "She's a difficult person to talk about accurately. About my marriage, now, I really think she's very serious. I really believe she's sincere. But she can't possibly suspect the effect she has on some people: you just have to admit it. I suppose I've seen her weaknesses too clearly to come under the spell, but on the other hand I'm glad I can feel her earnestness. In fact, mother's too earnest. The whole trouble is her lack of humor. You have it, and thank heaven I've inherited a little, but she hasn't any."

"Isn't that rich!" said Menelaos. "I wish I'd thought of that when she was having it out with the younger generation. Hermione, that's the absolute truth—she's terribly in earnest, and since she has no sense of humor, she's always liable to be earnest in the wrong direction."

"And she's so energetic," said Hermione. "If she got me once married, I wonder what she'd give her attention to next. I don't see how a person who looks so

serene, even placid at times, can be such a miracle of
energy. This frankness she's always talking of is just
an excuse to start something. I begin to understand now
what the old stories mean when they speak of a devastat-
ing beauty."

"Yes, that's your mother," said Menelaos. "I suppose
it's a gift. I dare say I waste time blaming her for it."

"But at least she ought to know herself better by this
time," said Hermione. "She ought to make allowance
for the way the susceptible will admire her and imitate
her. When you've conceded all you can, you can't excuse her entirely for misleading the innocent and the
unsuspecting."

"Oh, come, that's a trifle strong," said Menelaos.
"She doesn't mislead you, who I suppose are innocent,
and no one who knows her seems to be unsuspecting.
Every one, from the family gate-keeper to the neighbor-
ing gossips, seems to hope for the worst. Besides, the
curious thing is she has had her triumphs most often with
the sophisticated. At least they've been married. Paris
wasn't innocent nor unsuspecting."

"I was thinking of Adraste, that girl she's so fond
of," said Hermione. "I don't care for the type, but she
certainly is devoted to my mother, and I rather think
she'll imitate all her faults."

"What is Adraste's type?" said Menelaos. "Every
once in a while you talk like your mother—you refer to
some private notion of your own as though it were an
axiom any but a fool would know. I don't know what
types there are, nor which one is Adraste."

"Oh, she has what mother would call the love of life,
I suppose," said Hermione. "In plain words, she seems

to me—it isn't a nice thing to say of a girl, but I think she is rather passionate. You know what I mean—the unpleasant sense. If there were a man around and she were in love with him, I dare say she'd say yes after almost no courtship at all."

"Any man?" asked Menelaos. "Or is there a particular one?"

"Any one would do, I think," said Hermione. "Please understand I'm not saying anything against her. In fact I don't blame her—it's all mother's fault. If mother had taught her to control herself, to wait properly for love to come into one's life, not to be violent and unmaidenly! But from some remarks Adraste has dropped in my presence, I fancy she thinks romance justifies anything, and of course I couldn't argue with her—mother's example and all."

"Your own relation to Orestes has been a little informal, hasn't it?" said Menelaos.

"That's different," said Hermione. "Our relation has been exceptional, but proper throughout. I hardly feel that we had any courtship, we passed so quickly to exchanging advice about the family difficulties. You've no idea how admirable Orestes is; I shall always be glad I knew him first in emergencies—he's at his best under a strain. Of course, we've seen each other alone, when Eteoneus didn't know, but you were away, and we thought of ourselves as always destined for each other."

"You'll have to remind your mother about the destiny," said Menelaos. "Meanwhile—coming back to Adraste—I'm glad there's no man around just now, unless you count Damastor. Helen thinks he may be making love to Adraste."

"Nonsense!" said Hermione, "his mother has told me several times he's fond of me—rather foolish of him, you might say, but it indicates, at least, the type he admires. He's been carefully trained, and besides, he's only a boy. I doubt if he would marry out of his tradition, and even if he thought of it, he hasn't enough force of character yet to make love to Adraste, and face his mother. The sort of man I meant was Pyrrhus, perhaps; you might send for him after all, and marry him to Adraste. Then mother would have him in the family circle, as she desires, and I could take Orestes in peace."

"I won't have Pyrrhus," said Menelaos. "I'll tell her that again the moment I see her."

"Tell her now," said Hermione; "here she comes!"

III

"HELEN," said Menelaos, "I tell you again, I won't have Pyrrhus here!"

"I'm glad you mentioned Pyrrhus," said Helen; "I want to talk to Hermione about him, and it saves time to come straight to the point."

"Then let me tell you at once, mother," said Hermione, "I won't marry Pyrrhus—nor Damastor."

"Damastor? Heaven forbid!" said Helen.

"Didn't you ask her to marry him?" said Menelaos. "She understands that you did."

"Never in the world," said Helen. "I told her that Charitas said he was in love with her, and I remarked that she might do worse than take him. That's true, she might. But I want her to do better rather than worse. At the moment I was finding out whether Damastor had been paying his addresses to Hermione, as Charitas supposed. I learned what I suspected, that the boy was deceiving his mother. I have very little use for Damastor. As for Pyrrhus, I have not asked Hermione to marry him, and never shall. She may marry whom she chooses. She will, anyway. Indeed, I've never mentioned him to her, but I was about to tell her she ought to make his acquaintance before she chooses finally. You've been reporting our conversation, have you?"

"Yes," said Menelaos. "I told her you wanted Pyrrhus for a son-in-law, and you suggested having him here for a visit."

"No doubt the report had a good deal of your point of view in it," said Helen. "It's a familiar form of co-operation. Well, what do you think of the idea, Hermione?"

"Hermione agrees with me," said Menelaos, "that it's not safe to ask Pyrrhus here."

"Not safe?" said Helen. "Who's going to hurt him? Guests are always safe."

"But the host isn't, nowadays," said Menelaos. "We've made up our minds to practise some of your frankness. Hermione thinks with me that she and I wouldn't get much out of a visit from Pyrrhus. With you here, she wouldn't see much of him. He'd be charmed, of course—so deeply enchanted that he mightn't notice there was such a person as your daughter—or your husband. It won't do, Helen. You've come out all right so far, but from now on we'll leave well enough alone!"

"Mother, that isn't quite what I said. I—"

"I'm sure it isn't, daughter," said Helen. "Go on, Menelaos."

"There's nothing more," said Menelaos.

"There must be," said Helen. "No man can speak so to his wife, and before his daughter, without a great deal more. This is the way you insulted me the last time we discussed this subject. I told you then I would not stay with you if you repeated the offense. Now I shall go. I'm sorry, Hermione, to have you a witness of such unhappy clashes between your parents, but since your father is determined to have it so, perhaps it's as well you should know this episode at first hand. I asked your father to invite Pyrrhus here so that you might have a wider experience of society before you finally chose your husband. Your father accused me of having been in love with Achilles. I reminded Menelaos that I had never seen Achilles, who now is in his grave, but I said I surely would have loved him had I met him, for he was the greatest man of his time, and the most winning. We needs must love the highest when we see it, and if we don't wish to love it, we had better not see it. Pyrrhus is like his father, in my opinion; so far as I know, he's the finest man now in the world. Perhaps it would be kindness to you not to bring him here, if only we could be sure you never would see him, by chance, elsewhere; for you and Orestes are apparently content with each other. But some day you will see Pyrrhus, almost certainly, and what then, if you are bound already to another man? I wanted to say this to you, from my heart, and urge you to welcome Pyrrhus on this visit. I was going to add that though I think him superior to Orestes, I haven't seen Orestes, and I may be wrong. When you have met Pyrrhus you may think him less charming than I do. Whether the difference is the fault of my taste or the fault of yours, the incident in any event will be closed. After that, choose whom you like. But, Hermione, don't refuse to see Pyrrhus and then marry Orestes! Your faith in your husband will be poisoned from the beginning. You will remember you were unwilling to measure him alongside another man; you will wonder what would have happened if you had met Pyrrhus. At first you will pray you may never meet him, then you will wish you still might, and finally you'll meet him, of course. That's what I intended to say. But you and your father must arrange these matters now as you think best. I am leaving this house forever. It was understood between Menelaos and myself that if he spoke to me again in those terms I was to go."

"Oh, come now, Helen," said Menelaos, "I was off my guard."

"No, you weren't," said Helen, "though it would be no excuse if you were; I shouldn't think better of the insult for knowing it was spontaneous. But you went from talking to me, and from promising not to repeat such language, and you said the same thing again to my own daughter; now in her presence you tell me she agrees with you, and the child in self-defense has to explain she doesn't. We've come to the end, Menelaos; I'll go my way, and you go yours. Hermione, I ask you, on your honor, not to let your father start any story about a love-affair with Achilles, or any other falsehood to account for my leaving. I go because your father has his kind of mind."

"I suppose the disgrace which will fall on you and me is a small matter in your eyes," said Menelaos. "But at least you might consider the disgrace to Hermione, who is entirely innocent."

"No disgrace will fall on her," said Helen. "It will be only another instance of her misfortune in her parents. The disgrace, if there is any—of course there will be— will fall entirely on me."

"That's where it certainly ought to fall," said Menelaos, "but it won't—not entirely. I shall get some of it."

"None whatever," said Helen. "Your wife will

simply have left you for the second time. She will be in disgrace, and you will be ridiculous."

"I don't see that," said Menelaos.

"You will," said Helen. "When a husband or a wife runs away, the injured party, so-called, gets sympathy but no admiration, not even the first time it happens. People who can command love are not left behind. But if the desertion becomes a habit, there isn't even sympathy. The habitually deserted is laughed at."

"You mustn't go, Helen," said Menelaos, "you really must not."

"I am going," said Helen, "and I ask you to let me depart with some show of dignity in your manners, without words. Adraste and I can be ready to-morrow. I have several places in mind where we shall probably be welcome. There's Idomeneus—"

"Helen," said Menelaos, "I shan't try to use force to keep you here; perhaps it wouldn't succeed, if your determination is what you say it is. But I beg of you to stay. I surrender absolutely. I admit, before Hermione, I was altogether in the wrong. I have acted unworthily, I have—"

"Good-by," said Helen. "You have. But I am going."

"Mother," said Hermione, "if you'll stay, I'll do what you ask about Pyrrhus. I'll welcome him here, in this house, before I marry Orestes."

"You certainly ought to do that for your own sake, whether or not I stay," said Helen, "and I dare say your father will consent to invite him as soon as I'm gone. It will be safe then."

"He won't come if he hears there's another quarrel,"

said Hermione. "I'm sure he'll think father wants help in more wars."

"I've no doubt he'll think just that," said Helen. "I can hear him now. He has his father's hearty laugh."

"I suppose I must come to it," said Menelaos. "If you'll stay, Helen, I'll send the invitation to Pyrrhus at once."

"You ought to send it at once whether I go or stay," said Helen. "You know you ought. I'll make no bargain with you, never again. Send for him or don't send for him. The decision is now entirely yours. I was your wife an hour ago, trying to plan with you for our daughter. Now you are a free man, with all the choice and all the responsibility."

"I'll put it the other way around," said Menelaos. "If I send for him, will you stay?"

"You couldn't have heard what I said. I will make no bargain with you."

"Very well," said Menelaos. "You win. I'll send for Pyrrhus at once. Is that perfectly clear? At once. It's my own decision, entirely. I thought of it all myself. Nobody could persuade me not to. I'll go send the messenger now. . . . Will you stay?"

"You have made a wise decision," said Helen, "and you'd better go now and send the messenger."

"And you'll stay? That's the whole point!" said Menelaos.

"Oh, is it?" said Helen, "then it was a bargain, after all? In that case I won't stay."

"My word, what a woman!" said Menelaos. "I'll go send the messenger."

"Mother, you won't leave me, will you, till after Pyrrhus comes?" said Hermione. "I couldn't say it while father was here, but I dread being looked over as a possible wife, and I can't meet him naturally now, after all this talk. Besides, I shall feel like a hypocrite, with my mind already made up to marry Orestes."

"I promise to stay at least till Pyrrhus comes, or till Orestes comes," said Helen. "My own rule ought to work both ways; if you ought to see Pyrrhus first, I certainly ought to give Orestes a chance to prove himself what you think him. Your father is sending for Pyrrhus, but he's a long way off and can't arrive for some time. Meanwhile I should like to have your cousin here. Will you see to it that he comes?"

"There's nothing I'd rather do," said Hermione, "but I don't know where he is. I never know. He's hiding from Ægisthus. We'll just have to wait till he comes."

"Couldn't he trust you with his secret?" said Helen. "I don't like that at all. He will lose the best opportunity he is ever likely to have, if we can't find him at the critical moment. You have no means of getting a message to him?"

"None whatever," said Hermione, "but you mustn't blame him; he wanted to tell me where he hides, but I wouldn't let him. I had too many secrets of his already, and his life depended on this one. Besides, I got a sort of thrill out of his mysterious comings and goings—it was what a love-affair should be, I think, not regulated by ordinary information, but inspired by chance or providence or instinct."

"I know your temperament," said Helen. "Personally it wouldn't take the bloom off romance for me if I knew where my lover was. We'll have to wait till Orestes comes, then. I really hope it will be soon. And I want you to know, Hermione, I appreciate your willingness to do what I asked—to see Pyrrhus."

"Before I go," said Hermione, "I'd like to find out—I'm awfully curious—who that Idomeneus was. Father got quite excited at his name."

"He was one of my suitors," said Helen, "and perhaps you ought to know about him; for it's really because of him that I'm sure you do well to see Pyrrhus. When I was married the old custom still held for the suitors not to appear in person, but to send gifts with the offer of their hand, and let the lady and her parents decide. Of course you decided on some one you knew, or knew about. Idomeneus is a very original man. He was always far ahead of his times. He came himself with his gifts, and said that if he had the good fortune to win me, no one else should have the happiness of hearing the word of assent, and no one else should have the honor of bringing me to his home. Do you know, Hermione, I was so inexperienced then that I thought him most crude to go against the proper rules for a sentimental marriage. I rejected him first of all, and sent him off alone. Then I weighed the absentee suitors, conscientiously, conventionally, and as I felt, romantically, and I decided on Menelaos. Idomeneus is a strange person to this day. He has never married. But it's because of him that I think a girl should see all the possibilities, whether suitors or not, before she gives herself. Even at the best, we overlook so much!"

IV

"ALL day I've thought of you, Adraste," said Damastor. "You run in my head like a tune; whatever less lovely goes on round about me, I can always be silent and listen."

"I like to hear you say so, Damastor. How wonderful you are, with a pretty speech every time we meet, and never twice the same! To me you are a picture, not music; I dream of you—dreams so lively, I almost fear the household will see what I see, and know my secret."

"What do you see, Adraste?"

"Do you ask, my lover? . . . Damastor, your lips are cold! Poor boy!"

"Come farther into the shadow, Adraste—they will see us if we walk in the moonlight. I never saw such a great moon. Here, we can sit on this garden bench, and talk in peace."

"There never was such a moon, Damastor, but the brightness is you, I think; I have come here alone, nights like this, to see the garden turned to magic, and to think of—what we think of; but it was never so bright. If I could, I'd have it brighter still, and everybody here to see us walking in it. Our happiness is too beautiful to hide. I'm so proud of you, Damastor. . . Damastor, do you love me—as you said?"

"I love you more, Adraste, oh, so much more! Don't you feel it, how much I love you? Do we need words?"

"I like you to tell me, Damastor; nobody could tell it as you can. When you first told me you loved me—I shall never forget how you told me!"

"Adraste, I don't recall a single word. What I remember is the silence afterward. I was so afraid there might be some one else you cared for already, and you managed to let me know there was some one and just as I felt ready to die, I found out I was the one, after all."

"Yes, goosey, you found out! I had to tell you."

"You had to tell me! I like that. We just looked at each other and said nothing. I never was so happy in my life; I shall never be so happy again."

"Oh, I shall, Damastor. I didn't enjoy that silence a bit. I knew you cared, you innocent child, and I had to wait while you wrestled with the idea; and it wasn't news to me, whatever it was to you, that you had my heart. Really I was annoyed at you, just standing there paralyzed with your great discovery, and not knowing what to do next."

"If I was struck dumb, Adraste, it was with happiness. . . . And then I asked you for just one kiss, don't you remember?'

"I do; that was the precise number you asked for."

"But you let me take more than one, Adraste. I didn't know what kisses were."

"They frightened you a little, poor Damastor, didn't they? You seemed to think there were only so many kisses in the world, and if we took them all that day, there would never be any others. We had better save them up a little, you said. We promised to wait a long, long time for each other."

"How young it seems! We were both so young, Adraste!"

"Yes, it was several months ago. And now we are—what, dear lover?—middle-aged? At least so old that I grow retrospective, and sentimental, and I ask you to say again you love me, as you did when I was young."

"I ought to be a poet, Adraste, to say—"

"But you are, dear lover!"

"Ah, no! If I were, I might put a heart-ache into words. It is a heart-ache, isn't it! I wonder what brings it on—why happiness, I mean, should bring something so close to pain. I can't lay hold of my love, Adraste—I can't really touch you. My hand on your little fingers, on your soft cheeks, smooth and cool, all your softness in my arms—but you escape me, you whom I really love. Here in the shadow you are more real than sometimes when I see you in the broad day. Having you beside me, and listening to your voice, I can believe in the joy that surrounds me; sometimes in daylight I think it must be only a dream. I look at you and try to remember all that has happened, and I can't believe it. But I can recall your appearance as it was long ago—in memory or in a dream the picture of our love is clear, but often the actual moment seems illusion. Is it that way with you, Adraste?"

"You are a poet, I always say, Damastor—you have so much imagination, and you play with your experiences, ask questions of them, try to find words for them. I'm a very simple person—I'm just in love with you, all of me in love. It is dream enough for me to see you, here in the shadow, or in the moonlight, or in sunlight. Just to see you, to be at your side, to feel you near!"

"Adraste, do you remember the first time we met—that is, to meet? When my mother asked me to go for the jar of water, and asked you to help me, and you came along so demurely?"

"Your mother wouldn't ask me now to help you, would she! Do you remember that next time, when Helen brought me to your mother's house, and your mother sent me to the other end of the garden, and so arranged it herself, without meaning to, that you came out and talked to me?"

"Do I remember! My mother will never be the same person again, we gave her such a shock. Adraste, she still thinks I hadn't met you before; she insists she never asked you to help with that water-jar."

"Well, even if we hadn't met before, you might have come out."

"Mother thinks not—she thinks you bewitched me, got me there by magic. In a way she's right. But she oughtn't to say she didn't ask you to help, that other time."

"She didn't notice me, I suppose, Damastor—her mind was on the jar of water."

"You mean, she didn't notice how beautiful you were. When she saw that, the day in the garden, she was afraid of you."

"Am I so terrible, Damastor?"

"Fatal, I should say."

"It's love that's fatal, Damastor. . . . Damastor, have you thought out any plan for us yet—what we're to do?"

"I think of it all the time, Adraste, and the best thing still seems to wait a little longer, and keep our happiness, our happy secret, to ourselves. We couldn't be happier than we have been, and are—could we? The responsibility is mine, and I think I can manage my parents best if I don't break the news too suddenly; they're both terribly stubborn over any unexpected news they don't like. I can't think what else to do."

"Damastor, my dear lover, it's a happy secret, as you say—but I can't keep it much longer."

"You mean—you mean—"

"Of course I mean! There, don't be so frightened. I told you before, and now it's dawning on you, as our love did—it is our love again, isn't it! In a little while every one will know. Why shouldn't they? I'm happy and proud, Damastor; it's altogether beautiful. But I wish it weren't a secret! Why shouldn't we go right out and say to any who will listen, Damastor and Adraste are given to each other, given by their love, forever? I don't see what they could do, except envy us. Your mother wouldn't like me at first—she loves you too much to care for any girl who takes you away—but in time I could make her like me. Your father would be kind to us."

"Father would be kind, if he were alone," said Damastor, "but mother would be harder to convert than you think. She didn't like your beauty, to start with; she thinks that all beautiful women are probably bad, and if she knew what—what you just told me—she'd be sure her theory was sound. I'm sorry, Adraste, but it's a fact. She wouldn't understand. I keep hoping that if we wait there may be some way out. There'll be none if I speak now."

"Tell me this, Damastor—do you think I'm a bad

woman? Are you sympathizing at all with what you said would be your mother's view? Do you regret our love together?"

"Oh, Adraste, how can you ask me that!"

"How can I, dear? Because you suggest the question. You don't speak as you did when you wanted me first, when you said we'd face life together, when you were sure the only thing that mattered was that we should belong to each other. You weren't so prudent then—at least, you weren't so prudent for me, were you? I'm not saying I didn't want to love you—I mean that you were your very noblest then, when you took me, took your whole life in your own hands, I thought, faced any risk at all, of poverty, even of your mother's anger, in order that you might be yourself. Would you do it again, Damastor, if it were all still to be done?"

"Adraste, I love you so, what you say makes me feel a bit hurt, as though you were accusing me of unfaithfulness. Could I make it clearer to you than I have made it, how much I want you all to myself, our one life together? I can't see how I've done anything to disappoint you."

"In a way you have, Damastor, or I think you have; all I want is for you to prove me mistaken. I thought you knew your mind when you asked me to give myself—I thought you were giving yourself too. With such a man I could face anything. You can't know how utterly I admired you, Damastor. I knew your mother didn't like me, but we agreed we had the right to make our own choice and live our own lives. I imagined that you would go to her and simply say, with complete affection and respect, that you and I loved each other, that it was all settled; and you'd say it in some wonderfully wise words, so that your mother, even if she was sorry, would see it our way, or if she didn't, you would have the comfort of your own frankness and sincerity. Damastor, I'm disappointed that you do nothing at all— just wait. It isn't so brave nor so wise as I expected you to be, and at times I fear you are less sure of yourself than you were. Did I misjudge you, I ask? Or did you love me once, and have you changed?"

"How much I love you, Adraste, I'll give my life to showing. If I've delayed, it isn't because I'm a coward. It will take courage to face my mother, but when I'm sure it's the right time I'll speak to her. Have you told Helen?"

"Not a word."

"Does she suspect?"

"Damastor, Helen seems to know everything of this sort that goes on around her, so I dare say she has guessed long ago, but she has said nothing to me, and of course I haven't spoken to her."

"If you feel that way toward Helen, you ought to understand why I too wish to keep it a secret for a while longer."

"I don't want to keep it a secret from anybody, Damastor, but I want you to tell it. I want you to boast of it, and be proud, so that I can be proud of you."

"Aren't you proud of me, Adraste?"

"Damastor, I dare say no man ever quite knows why a woman loves him; so far as I can judge from what you say, you entirely miss the things I love you for. I love the courage in you to know at sight what belongs to your nature, to your own destiny. Most people seem to be imitating each other, without considering whether anything they do is what they really want. You have what Helen often speaks of, you have the love of life; you naturally try to see things as they are, you hate subterfuge and hypocrisy, you would be frank with yourself and with others. That's why I loved you, Damastor—I could never love the opposite kind of man. You mustn't lose your great gift, Damastor; if you should change, I couldn't be proud of you—I should be fond of you always, but, oh, so sorry for you! It isn't simply this one problem, you see—it's your whole life that's at stake, for if you begin now to hide your thoughts and your feelings, and to cringe before the opinions of other people, you'll be lost forever—I'm sure of that, Damastor. It's so terribly simple, I thought you of all persons would see it clearly. If you have done what you now think was wrong, of course you ought to stop and do what you now think is right. That's why I asked you whether you regretted our love. But if what we did is still right, as we believed it to be, there's no reason on earth why we should hide it from anybody. If others don't like what we are and what we do, of course we wish there were no such difference of opinion, but sooner or later we have to decide who's controlling our lives—ourselves or those others. When I thought you and I were to make our own choices, I was proud of you, Damastor."

"I don't blame you for misjudging me, Adraste, but you do misjudge me. I have told you again and again that I would let no one, not even my parents, control my destiny. If I could go to them now, as you want me to, and tell them I've chosen you for my future wife, whether they like it or not, and if they would calmly sub-

mit, as you half hope they would, then I suppose you'd be
convinced that I'm a forceful character. But if I tell my
father this news, with mother so fixed in her prejudices,
he'll turn me out of the house—and where are we to go?
I don't see the heroism of that. Love of life—yes, but
first of all we must live. Temporarily, at least, we are
both better off than we'd be if my people sent me away
and I had no shelter or protection to offer you."

"Must one live, Damastor—is that the thing of first
importance? How we live, I'd rather say. I think the
love of life must have in it a kind of recklessness, a determination not to pay too high for mere existence—not to
pay with your soul. My way would be to go hand in
hand with you now, and tell them all about it. First we'd
find Helen and tell her, then we'd go to your people; and
if they disowned us, as you expect, then we'd literally
walk down the road together till something happened to
us—some good fortune or perhaps some bad. That
would be the sincere and fine thing to do, I'm sure.
Wouldn't you, in your heart, be happy to do that with
me? Damastor, will you do it now—this very hour?"

"What a wild idea, Adraste!—to go off that way, like
tramps, with you—you couldn't stand it; you'd die before we had gone far!"

"I shall die here. But I'd rather die that way, with
the man I thought I gave myself to. Damastor, I know
to-night that I have lost you."

"I'll never leave you, Adraste! To-night you are full
of gloomy thoughts and fears, but there's no reason for
them, except that you aren't quite yourself. You'll wake
up rested to-morrow, and remember what we have said,
and all the grim things you said to me, and you'll laugh

at your worries. I shall always love you, Adraste; I
love you absolutely. I'll make you proud of me yet, when
the right moment comes to speak, and you see at last that
I was right. . . . Don't go—we have lost the hour talking of these stupid matters. I thought we were to be
together, just to be happy, and here we've been arguing."

"Will you walk to the house with me, Damastor, or
would you prefer that I go back alone? Very probably
Helen will see us, or Menelaos, or Hermione."

V

"Now that I've sent for him," said Menelaos, "I want to tell you one thing. I was wrong, and all that, but you had no right to thrash out the question as you did, in the presence of our child. There can't be any discipline in a house where that sort of wrangling goes on in public. I detest family disputes above all things, and the worst possible is between parents with their own children listening."

"I regret it too," said Helen, "but it seemed better than to accept without protest the insult you laid on me before my daughter. You have a curious point of view, Menelaos. You brought me home, it seems, for the satisfaction of saying unspeakable things during the rest of my life, and you appear to think, for some reason, that I will put up with it. You seem to think it is good for your child and your household to hear such unmanly discourtesy from your lips. If I am not mistaken, you even think it is good for your own character. Every time you insult me, you give the impression of feeling morally elevated."

"Helen, I haven't said a word before my own household; no self-respecting man would do that. When Eteoneus wanted to open the subject, I refused to let him go on."

"What subject did Eteoneus wish to open?" said Helen.

"That's ancient history," said Menelaos. "I was foolish to mention it."

"You were," said Helen, "but since you did, I hope you will tell me what Eteoneus wanted to say."

"I'm sorry, Helen, but I can't. It wasn't important, anyway."

"Menelaos, I suspect it was very important. In any case, it concerns me, and it is of a nature that you prefer to hide from me."

"Well, I can't tell you, that's all there is to it. I don't wish to, in the first place, and if I did repeat his remarks, you'd accuse me of insulting you, and before I got out of the mess, I'd have to invite some other guest to the house. We haven't enough food in the storeroom to entertain any more; it was a disappointing harvest, you remember."

"I won't be put off this way," said Helen. "If you decide not to tell me, I'll ask Eteoneus what he said."

"Since when have you gone to the gate-keeper for opinions on your own character, Helen? Really, you couldn't do anything more disgraceful than that, to talk over our affairs with the servants!"

"I have no intention of discussing our affairs—I'll merely ask him what mysterious thing it was he said about me."

"He'll tell you, of course!" said Menelaos.

"I don't know whether he will or not, but I can ask him. I'd rather have it from you, of course, but since the servants are whispering things about me, and since you won't share the information you have, I refuse to remain in the dark."

"Helen, I see I've made too much of a small matter.

I'll tell you the little there is to tell. On my return, Eteoneus asked me just what the attitude of the servants should be to you. They were surprised, he said, that you came back at all, and still more that you were here again as though—well, as though you had never been away. They were prepared, on my return, to cheer my lonely life, he said, but they didn't know how to meet a situation in which there seemed to be no loneliness, and no need for cheering up. They felt, he said,—"

"When was it you stopped him—prevented him from going on?" said Helen. "That's quite a speech already."

"He made it against my will, and rather piece-meal," said Menelaos. "I kept bringing him back to the subject, but he would digress, and—"

"What was the subject you kept bringing him back to?" said Helen.

"Why, he came in to talk about Hermione," said Menelaos.

"What?"

"About Hermione and Orestes," said Menelaos. "He was worried over their intimacy."

"I can't believe my ears," said Helen. "You, who never discuss your wife with the servants, you only discuss your daughter with them—your daughter and her love-affairs! There's a distinction, I suppose, but I can't see it. Menelaos, I had no idea you had lost your fineness of feeling! You had it once—what has happened to you? And what will become of us all? At your age, if you begin developing such weaknesses, you will soon deteriorate quite beyond rescue, and your influence on Hermione will be most unfortunate. There's no cure for vulgarity."

"If you'd been in the room when Eteoneus was talking," said Menelaos, "you'd know well enough that I wasn't gossiping about my family—not about my wife nor my daughter—nor about my brother nor his wife, nor his son. I speak so particularly in order that I may not be accused of evasion. Eteoneus doesn't like Orestes, and he came to poison my mind against the boy. Orestes involved Hermione, of course, and the gatekeeper told me the young people had met constantly during our absence. I told him they had been promised to each other long ago, that I would place the fullest confidence in my daughter's discretion, and that he himself was an impertinent old meddler. I sent him back to his post, but he's a stubborn fellow and it took some time to get rid of him. He kept talking all the while, trying to draw something out of me with reference to you. I refused to listen to him, but before I got him out he had made his point of view clear enough. What I told you was a summary, more concise than his remarks. He feels that the world is departing from the traditions he grew up in; what he really came for was to be comforted against the consciousness and the consequences of growing old."

"He's probably right about Orestes," said Helen, "and the world is changing. I'm sorry it is. Conservative ways, conventional manners, are best in the end. It may be necessary to depart from them, but those who depart must pay a big price, I should think. That's why I regret to see you give up your old courtliness, Menelaos. It was one of your happiest accomplishments, and though rougher, more downright behavior is coming into fashion, it will never sit so well on your nature, in my

opinion. I noticed the change immediately that night in
Troy, when we met again. I admired Agamemnon for
staying and making those sacrifices. There was something about it—I don't know—a tone, you might say; it
indicated the hold his breeding had on him. I was sorry
you didn't stay and do the same thing. Our return has
not been so happy as a home-coming should be. You began it in the wrong mood."

"I can't see that at all," said Menelaos. "Our troubles are in our own character, I think. Sacrifices are
very well; I sacrificed with Agamemnon for a whole
day. But if you overdo that sort of thing you cease to
be religious, or conventional, and become fanatic, or even
foolish. The war was finished; our business, as I saw
it, was to take up our interrupted lives again. I don't
know what got into Agamemnon; he usually is no stick-
ler for rites and ceremonies. I teased him a bit about
Clytemnestra—suggested he was afraid to go home and
face her. Considering what really has happened in his
house, I wish I hadn't said just that. He'll recall it when
he arrives, and perhaps he'll imagine I'm on his wife's
side in this bad business. But he isn't back yet—notice
that, Helen. We came in fairly good time, allowing for
delays of the wind, but he isn't heard of. If our attitude
toward the sacrifices counted for or against us, he ought
to have got home first, don't you think?"

"I never saw any connection between the sacrifices
and the speed of the boat," said Helen. "The question,
as I understood it, was whether we were to get home at
all. You didn't make much headway, you remember, until we had those formal sacrifices in Egypt. Agamemnon
will soon be back, I've no doubt, and we'll have a sound
explanation of his delay."

"When he has had time to get settled," said Menelaos, "we'll ask him here to talk about Hermione and Orestes."

"That will make another guest," said Helen. "Menelaos, are you sure you've sent for Pyrrhus, as you said you would?"

"Certainly; the messenger went off that day—within the hour. Pyrrhus will be here on a friendly visit—that's all we agreed on, you remember, and we'll have Orestes too. Not at the same time, of course: before, don't you think?"

"I'd like to see Orestes, if he can be found," said Helen, "but Hermione doesn't know where he is. I feel as you do that we should meet him before we come to a decision. And really I've no objection to Agamemnon. Since we all used to talk of the children's marriage to one another, I dare say both sides of the house had better take part in the discussion now. . . . There's the gate-keeper coming up the walk. Shall I leave you two?"

"Stay here," said Menelaos. "I don't know what he wants. See for yourself whether I'm too intimate with him."

"Menelaos, may I speak to him about—what he said of me?"

"You may not," said Menelaos.

"Why not? Didn't you give me the correct version?"

"Didn't I what? Oh, you think I invented it, for my own uses! Think so, if you like! But I told the truth."

"Menelaos," said Eteoneus, "I expected to find you alone. I beg your pardon."

"Perhaps I'm in the way, Menelaos," said Helen. "I'll return when you are at liberty again."

"See here, Eteoneus, what do you mean by saying you expected to find me alone? What has come over you? Do you take it amiss that I'm talking in my own house to my own wife?"

"I presume to take nothing amiss with you, Menelaos," said Eteoneus, "no matter what's in the back of my thoughts."

"That won't do, Eteoneus," said Menelaos. "I told you the other day you'd have to keep a civil tongue when you spoke of any member of my household. You understood me clearly, I believe?"

"No, Menelaos," said the gate-keeper, "I heard the words clearly, but I didn't understand you. . . . But we'd better not go on, with my lady here."

"Eteoneus," said Helen, "I shall be glad to hear whatever you wish to say. Say it as if I were not present—unless it is some private business of my husband's, which I ought not to know. You are an old friend, and I don't feel that I've seen much of you since my return. How have you been?"

"My health has been excellent," said Eteoneus, "but I have a troubled mind."

"I'm sorry for that," said Helen. "Such faithful service as you have given, ought to leave you, at your years, with a quiet conscience."

"Oh, nothing the matter with my conscience. It's not my own wrong-doing I have to worry about."

"Eteoneus," said Menelaos, "what brought you here? What do you wish with me?"

"One moment, Menelaos," said Helen. "Do I understand that Eteoneus is troubled by the wrongs others have done?"

"That's it exactly," said Eteoneus.

"You mean, wrongs that people have done to you personally?" said Helen. "Of course I don't want to seem prying into your affairs."

"No offense at all," said Eteoneus. "No, not wrongs done to me personally."

"Well," said Helen, "when you come to think of it, there are a frightful number of wrongs in the world done by others, to others than ourselves. What a passion for grief you must have, Eteoneus, to borrow all that trouble!"

"Eteoneus," said Menelaos, "I insist on knowing what—"

"I beg your pardon, Menelaos," said Helen. "I did not realize that my talking to Eteoneus was annoying you."

"Not at all," said Menelaos. "Talk to him all you like—at another time. Now I wish to hear his errand."

"It's merely a bit of news," said Eteoneus, "but there was a time when you would have been glad to hear it."

"You don't mean that Pyrrhus has declined the invitation?"

"He hasn't received it yet. No, my news has to do with your brother."

"Is he back?"

"He is," said Eteoneus. "The news has just come that he's home again, safe and in the usual health. The man who told me—he passed through here about an hour ago—actually saw him draw up with his chariots before his own door, with all the baggage and the prizes—and with Cassandra, his handsome slave. The man said Cassandra is very beautiful."

"She is said to be," replied Menelaos. "What happened next?"

"Nothing. They all went into the house. After the doors were closed the crowd waited a while, of course, and then went about their business. The man continued his journey."

"I'd like to know what went on behind those doors," said Menelaos.

"So should I," said Eteoneus, "but the man apparently missed the significance of the whole episode. He's only a casual trader, and he hadn't heard of Clytemnestra's conduct. He was quite surprised when I told him; he deeply regrets now that he came away just—as you might say—at the moment of greatest possibilities."

"Didn't he see Clytemnestra at all?" said Menelaos.

"Oh, yes, she came out to meet Agamemnon, and led him into the house, the man said. She greeted Cassandra, too, very considerately."

"She did, did she?" said Menelaos. "And was Ægisthus doing the honors too?"

"The man didn't see him—nor even hear of him," said the gate-keeper. "That's because he passed through the place so hurriedly."

"Eteoneus," said Menelaos, "when you first told me about Clytemnestra and Ægisthus, I thought the whole rumor might very well be sheer fiction, and I said so. Now I wonder whether my suggestion hasn't been proved sound! If Ægisthus were master in the house, Clytemnestra wouldn't have welcomed Agamemnon home in that dutiful fashion. If there had been a scandal, your trader would have heard of it, no matter how short a time he stayed."

"Oh, nonsense, Menelaos," said Helen, "you are trying to deceive yourself. Orestes told Hermione all about it, Hermione told me, as no doubt she told you. Eteoneus has known of it before any of us. No, my sister is living with Ægisthus, and her husband has come home. The trader quite evidently moved on too soon. By this time they've all reached some sort of understanding. How I should like to know what it is!"

"There's only one kind of understanding," said Menelaos. "My brother will kill Ægisthus, and Clytemnestra will want to kill Cassandra. Eteoneus, tell the men to get my things ready for an immediate journey. I'll go at once to my brother."

"If you ought to go," said Helen, "I shan't try to keep you, but I have a presentiment that you'd better stay here. Whatever has happened, has happened already; you'd be too late to help. Messengers better informed are sure to bring news. I'd stay here, if I were you."

"There's something in what you say, Helen, but I ought to go. I must see for myself how it has been settled."

"If you are worrying about Agamemnon," said Helen, "I'd send for news at once, but I wouldn't go myself. You'd be of no use, if he's in trouble, unless you took a considerable company of your men with you, and you'd look rather foolish marching in with your troops if by any chance Agamemnon and Clytemnestra have made it up."

"They can't make it up," said Menelaos.

"Oh, I wouldn't go so far as that," said Helen. "Almost any reconciliation is possible in this world. Send Agamemnon a greeting, as though you knew nothing of the Ægisthus incident; ask him to come here at the first opportunity. His answer will give you the news and guide your actions."

"Suppose he is reconciled to Clytemnestra and brings her along?" said Menelaos.

"Well, if he is reconciled to her, he may bring her," said Helen. "She's my sister, when all's said and done, and she's the mother of the young man you're determined to have for a son-in-law. You can't ignore her. Now, if you had seen the matter my way, and had thrown your influence toward Pyrrhus, you would have spared yourself this embarrassment."

"I never liked Clytemnestra," said Menelaos. "Whether they are reconciled or not, I shall always feel that her conduct was peculiarly offensive. . . . I dare say the messenger is the right thing— Eteoneus, tell one of the men to get ready. Tell him at once."

"Well, what do you think of it, Helen?"

"I don't know, Menelaos. It's your brother and my sister. What it will mean to us, I don't know."

"I'm not thinking of us," said Menelaos. "We'll stand any shock, I dare say. I didn't like to show my feelings before Eteoneus. There'll be terrible doings in that house . . . don't you think?"

"I think there have been, by this time," said Helen. "I'm sorry for Electra, and for Orestes. And I'm sorry for Hermione. She'll take it much to heart, and such things ought not to be occupying a young girl's mind. . . Menelaos, what did you make of that trader Eteoneus pretended to quote?"

"Why, what should I make of him? Just what Eteoneus told us."

"You believed the account, then. I thought you did. I didn't. Eteoneus knows more than he told us, or the trader knew more than he told Eteoneus. As you said yourself, any trader would hear the scandal, no matter how short a time he stayed, and if he heard it, he wouldn't leave so carelessly."

"You think Eteoneus knows more than he told us?"

"Eteoneus or the trader."

"I'll call him back this minute and find out!"

"Ask him whether I wasn't right to advise you to stay at home," said Helen. "And ask him for his reasons. I'll go tell Hermione the news. Perhaps it concerns her most."

"Menelaos," said Eteoneus, "I've been looking through the door till your wife should leave the room. Now I can speak to you alone. I didn't tell you all."

"Then tell me now—what's the rest of it?"

"The trader knew the scandal, all right—that part was an invention of mine. He wanted to stay and see what happened, but he says every one in town told him to move on, if he valued his health."

"His health?"

"His life, if you want it plainly. The trader said Clytemnestra and Ægisthus had the scene all set to trap Agamemnon, and they preferred to do it without witnesses."

"Get the men together, Eteoneus! I'll go at once."

"I wouldn't, Menelaos, if I were you. I hope it's not necessary. I've been trying to find Orestes, and I rather think I've got word to him. In fact, I know I have. He'll tend to it. He doesn't consider me his friend, but in an emergency like this I like him well enough, and now he has his chance to show what kind of son he is. It's his right, more than yours, to be with Agamemnon now. If I'm not mistaken, he's already well on his way. You'd better stay here, send your messenger, and wait till you have the reply."

"Where was Orestes? I thought he couldn't be found?"

"I didn't want to find him before," said Eteoneus. "It's his secret, so I won't say where he was, but now we'll see what he's made of. You won't mind, I hope, but I fitted him out with some of your best weapons. It's all in the family, as I said to him."

VI

"HERMIONE, my dear, I came as soon as I heard the news. I hope Helen is at home."

"She isn't, Charitas—she's out this afternoon, I'm sorry to say. Come in and let me be a poor substitute."

"Dear child, not poor at all! But this is the second time I've missed her. If I didn't know your mother so well, I'd suspect she was avoiding me. You'll tell her how disappointed I am. The moment I heard that Agamemnon was back, I said I must come right over and tell Helen how glad I was. . . . Dear me! . . . You've heard from your aunt, I suppose?"

"No, we haven't heard from any of them directly. A man brought the news that Agamemnon is home again. Mother told me. Father has sent him an invitation to spend a few days with us as soon as he's at leisure."

"Your uncle, Hermione, is a very distinguished man. You ought to be proud of him. I don't mean, of course, that your father isn't distinguished too, but Agamemnon always had . . . well, there was a certain something about him. It's hard to define personality. I never could understand why your aunt didn't appreciate what she had—most women would think themselves well off with such a husband."

"Perhaps she doesn't want to be well off," said Hermione. "Mother always seems annoyed when one speaks respectfully of ordinary comforts and of an established life. They seem to have their own notion of success. But I ought not to speak so of my aunt. I dare say she does appreciate her husband—what she has seen of him. I know nothing to the contrary."

"My dear child, you don't mean to pretend you haven't heard how Clytemnestra's been going on! Of course you have! It's the most general subject of conversation among all the friends of the family. I don't know where women get the courage to do such things. Not that I want that kind of courage! But you can't say she appreciates Agamemnon if she's living with Ægisthus."

"I don't feel that I know much about such things, Charitas, but I fancy I can understand my aunt's point of view, at least to a degree. I don't defend the irregularities in her conduct, but she has her good qualities. Orestes—my cousin, you know—is devoted to her, and I always remind myself that so fine a man wouldn't care for a person with no virtues whatever."

"Perhaps he's merely dutiful," said Charitas. "In any case, I'm glad to hear that of Orestes; I had thought him perhaps a bit too advanced in his ideas. You know, he didn't go to Troy, though he is quite formidable, they say, in the field. Some one told me—who was it?—that he stayed home because he didn't approve of the war. I feared he might be temperamentally disloyal. But Clytemnestra seems to me undoubtedly—I don't suppose your uncle will take her back? You said you hadn't heard."

"She is back, isn't she?" said Hermione. "She never was away. I dare say they'll quarrel, but I repeat, Clytemnestra has some things on her side, and I reserve my judgment till I know much more than at present I do."

"Has she something on her side? I didn't know that! Has Agamemnon been—? Well, it's not to be wondered at; men always are. Do tell me, Hermione! I've missed it entirely—I don't see how."

"It's perfectly simple," said Hermione, "if you know them both. Agamemnon is high-handed, and Clytemnestra is high-spirited. What more do you need for a quarrel? Orestes says his mother resented a little all the excitement over my mother. You might guess she was jealous, but Orestes says not; he says his mother merely thought the expedition to Troy was—well, out of proportion. Then there was Iphigeneia. Haven't you heard about that? It was long ago, when they were trying to get the boats off. My uncle was at Aulis, and he sent for Iphigeneia to come and marry Achilles. My aunt was naturally delighted with the match, and was packing up to go on with her daughter, when Agamemnon sent word he wanted only the daughter—her mother mustn't come. That was rather intolerable, don't you think? Clytemnestra wanted her daughter to be well married, but she counted on being asked to the wedding. You wouldn't believe how brutal Agamemnon was about it—said that if Clytemnestra appeared, there would be no marriage, and she mustn't ask questions, but he would explain after he got home. Rather than spoil Iphigeneia's chance, Clytemnestra sent her on to Aulis alone—and there was no marriage, after all. Clytemnestra thought that such a betrayal ended her obligations to Agamemnon. I'm not prepared to say she was wrong."

"I don't see why, because the wedding fell through, she should break up the home," said Charitas. "If I went off with another man every time my husband failed to do what he promised, I'd—well, I'd not be what I am. Iphigeneia could have found another husband."

"No, she couldn't," said Hermione. "They did a dreadful thing—they offered her as a sacrifice for a favorable wind."

"Hermione! How awful! And I suppose it wasn't favorable, after all."

"Yes, it was," said Hermione. "That's when they sailed for Troy. But perhaps they didn't really kill her. I used to believe they did, but no one admits it now, and there's another story, more recent, about her being still alive, in some obscure place. Why she should be there and not at home, I can't guess. But whatever happened to her, I hope my uncle has explained it satisfactorily by this time, and I do hope he'll see that his failure to explain earlier justified Clytemnestra in abandoning her home ties. Orestes says—"

"Hermione, my dear, I doubt if Orestes is a good influence upon you; he seems to talk—and think—as I should expect of his mother's child. You never would express such disturbing theories if some one had not imposed them on you; it's not in your sweet nature. I suspect Orestes. I hope you won't allow yourself to admire him too much!"

"I doubt if I admire him too much," said Hermione.

"I'm sure you don't," said Charitas. "Really, Hermione, it's a mystery to me how you have kept your ideas of life so steady and so high, with such extraordinary performances going on around you. You know I'm devoted to your mother, but—you won't mind my saying what even those who love her best agree in—she's not an ideal parent. She's too much preoccupied with love, as if that were the whole thing in life. Common sense goes further, I say. And a little skill to plan and contrive. These people who give way to their feelings, Hermione, they're simply a burden on the rest of us. Such respect as they have for their instincts and their impulses! I hope you'll never go in for an emotional career. I've always tried to suppress Damastor's impulses, or at least to keep his mind off them. So far I flatter myself I've succeeded. Don't you think he's a dear boy, Hermione?"

"I haven't seen enough of him, Charitas, to know whether he's a dear boy or not. He's very civil to me when we meet."

"Civil? Why, Hermione, he's devoted to you—he's really dead in love with you! There's no reason why you should be coy about it—with his mother, your old friend. I know his feelings on the subject. That child tells me everything. He often stops in my room to talk after he has been over to see you."

"What does he tell you, Charitas? Because, he never comes to see me. I haven't had a word with him for weeks and weeks."

"Hermione! I feel faint! Damastor! . . . Don't tell me that—the boy wouldn't deceive me."

"Charitas, I'm sorry to tell you, but once before, or several times, you've hinted that Damastor was in love with me. I couldn't discuss a hint of that sort, but it worried me, because Damastor has shown no interest in me at any time. I didn't like you to have a false impression."

"He said—he always says—merely that he is coming over here to see you. I thought he meant—"

"I think he meant he was coming over here," said

Hermione. "I don't doubt he came. And I don't doubt he's infatuated with a girl. There's more than one woman in this house, Charitas."

"Don't tell me it's—your mother!"

"No, for a wonder, it's not. My guess is—of course I don't know— it's Adraste."

"And who is Adraste?"

"You know—you've seen her—the girl who attends my mother."

"The one who came with Helen to my garden? Hermione! She's very beautiful."

"She certainly is—if you like the type."

"How awful! I dare say she has no character at all. She's a nobody, at best. And constantly with Helen! . . . Hermione, why do you think Damastor's infatuated with her?"

"They've been together a good deal—I've seen them walking and talking, when they perhaps supposed themselves alone. He's only a boy, Charitas, and she's a scheming little thing, if I guess right. She knows her charms, and would rather die than not use them, and I doubt if she has any morals to speak of. I may be wrong, but I imagine Damastor has fallen into her clutches."

"My poor boy! My poor boy! I might have known. This is your mother's doings, Hermione! I'd spare your feelings if I could, but I must say that woman has paid me shabbily for my loyalty to her—even when I knew she didn't deserve it. What right has she to come back among honest women, who have put up with worse husbands, perhaps, than she ever had, and air herself as if she were a goddess, beyond human measures of right and wrong—and bring with her this little snake, to charm away our men and poison our lives! If your mother had her just reward, Hermione! Well, I can save Damastor yet. I'll send him away where that girl can't get her hands on him. He'll forget her if he sees a little more of the world. I'll send him to my brother's, for a visit. If she ever speaks to him again, it will be at my funeral!"

"On the whole, I think you're wise," said Hermione. "Damastor is too nice a boy, I'm sure, to have his life spoiled by the wrong kind of woman. I'd be sorry for any well brought up man who chose Adraste. I'm glad that Orestes, so far as he knows about her, doesn't like her at all."

PART THREE
THEIR ELDERS

THEIR ELDERS

I

"IF YOU insist on knowing my reasons," said Hermione, "they are three, as nearly as I can take an inventory at short notice. In the first place, I don't love him. In the second place, I do love Orestes. In the third place, Pyrrhus is a good deal of a brute, from all I have heard, and the strong-handed sort of husband doesn't appeal to me. I wonder that you continue the discussion. Let Pyrrhus come; I will look at him, as you wish, and then he can go home. All this talk makes me care less for him every day."

"If my object were merely to arrange a marriage between you and Pyrrhus," said Helen, "I certainly would not talk so much about it; I realize that the effect may be as you say. You may come to hate the sound of his name, and you may develop a strong dislike for me. When you see him, perhaps you will like him in spite of all that I have said in his favor. But however that may be, I wish you to become acquainted with a few plain truths about marriage, which most girls learn too late. It is your education I have set my heart on, even more than your marriage. If there were another way to bring the ideas to your mind, I wouldn't put them into words. Forgive me if I weary you, Hermione. Perhaps you could understand my point of view, if you made the effort; we of the elder generation have a point of view, you know. It comes from having brought children into the world. We wish to give them a better life than we had. The only way is to put our experience at their disposal. But nothing annoys the young so much. Now I don't pretend to know everything about love, but I know a great deal more than you do, and your three reasons for not considering Pyrrhus seem to me absurd. Don't be angry! Some day they will seem so to you, even though you continue to love Orestes."

"They don't seem absurd to me now," said Hermione, "and I'm the one who has to decide."

"You are," said Helen, "and I want you to decide with your eyes open, without deceiving yourself. You don't love Pyrrhus, you say. Why should you? You haven't met him. But he is coming here in a few weeks. I'm not asking you to lose your heart to him; I'm giving you fair warning that though you haven't seen him, and though you are now, as you think, in love with another man, you may wish you belonged to Pyrrhus, body and soul, twenty-four hours after you have met him. Don't think you are the one woman in history to whom that could not happen."

"If you mean that Orestes isn't so remarkable a person as Pyrrhus," said Hermione, "I am willing to accept your opinion. That is, I don't agree with it, but I don't mind your thinking so. You may be quite right. But that is no reason why I should hesitate a moment where my heart is committed once for all. Some men and some women are made for each other. I believe there is a destined mate for each one of us, if we are only lucky enough to find each other. Orestes and I are mates, that's all there is to it. Pyrrhus may be as wonderful as you say, but he is not my fate. It's no use arguing; I feel it."

"You feel that Orestes and you," said Helen, "were fashioned and preserved for each other, the product and climax of happy stars? I know the feeling well. I've had it several times, for different men. It's nature's fine way of saying that at the moment we want him very much. Haven't you ever seen a child, at first sight of a doll, clasp it to her arms and cry, 'That's my doll?' What we want very much always seems destined."

"You don't believe in people being spiritual mates?"

"They may become so in time," said Helen, "but it takes a great deal of adjustment, so much so that rather than be pessimistic about the accuracy of heavenly patterns, I'd rather say there are no predestined couples, no separated parts which brought together make a harmonious whole. You can't believe that spiritual mate nonsense, my daughter, after the experience of having two or more sincere men in love with you at once. Both think you are their fate, and when you choose one, the other will never be convinced that you knew what your fate was. Very probably you didn't. And certainly you can't believe the theory after you find yourself in love a second time—the same passion, the same heart-ache, the same sense of destiny—but another man. When we are young we all are inclined to believe in the one person intended for us, and when we learn that our devoted hearts can break a second time, or even a third, we despise ourselves. Then gradually we come to accept the order of nature, that love can strike again and again, as our personalities develop and change, and our destinies are not so final as we supposed them to be."

"Mother, you talk as though nothing were stable in this world," said Hermione. "I can't agree; it seems impious. I prefer to be loyal."

"Nothing is stable in this world, Hermione, unless we ourselves are so," said Helen. "Loyalty is an achievement in our character—you don't find it growing around you like a plant, or hitting you like lightning. There's a world of difference between loyalty and love. Lovers are often loyal, from youth to old age, and their constancy is all the more admired for not being natural. When once you marry, love may leave you, but the problem of loyalty never will. I want you to choose the man to whom it will be easiest in the long run for you to be loyal, and I insist it's more a matter of choice than you think. You say you are in love with Orestes now, and you can't resist this fatal passion. I warn you, though of course you won't believe me, that you may be quite as much in love later with some one else. You would tell me, I'm sure, that the second love can be resisted and should be. I agree that it can be—and so can the first."

"If you are drawing on your experience to advise me," said Hermione, "I'd like to ask you more about your life than seems quite proper; I doubt if a girl ought to ask such things of her mother."

"I'll tell you anything I know," said Helen, "and you are welcome to ask anything you can think of."

"Well, if you feel this way about love," said Hermione, "I can't see why you didn't stay with my father. You could very well have resisted your love for Paris; you could have set me an example of loyalty. I am confused, I must confess, between what you have done and what you advise."

"Dear child," said Helen, "there's no connection between them!"

"That's what I thought," said Hermione.

"No, indeed," said Helen. "I should never in the world advise you to do what I've done. It would be useless. You couldn't do it. And even if you could, you haven't my reasons for it."

"I agree that I couldn't imitate your life," said Hermione, "but I don't think you ought to say it as though it were a gift which I didn't inherit. We shall never think the same way as to what kind of life is desirable. I fear I can't imagine any reason which would justify your going off with Paris."

"I had no intention of justifying my life, Hermione—neither to you nor to anybody else. But your question made me think of the reasons for my actions, whether they are justified or not. Let me advise you not to justify your life after it is lived; at that stage it will speak for itself. And don't judge the past actions of other people—it's too late to change them. You seem to me a little censorious as you pronounce upon my career. I object not because it's my career, but because any final verdicts on others seem presumptious for a human being to make. I discuss your life so much because it is still in the future; what you have once done, however, I shall say nothing about."

"I meant no discourtesy," said Hermione, "and I do see why you are different from other people. You are so beautiful that ordinary rules seem not to apply."

"They didn't apply," said Helen, "but they ought to have done so, and I wanted them to. That is the whole trouble. I never wanted to be different from my fellows,

and yet I've never felt that I was living in the same world
with them. Can't you see how the situation would arise,
and how fatal it would be? No one has the right to shut
us out from any part of life, not even from hard things,
from the sorrows and sufferings. They always said I was
beautiful, but the only effect I could notice was that they
treated me as if I weren't a human being. My whole life
has been an attempt to put myself back among other people, to make sure I wasn't missing anything. I resented
being excused from the ordinary rules of life. If I did
wrong when I was a child, I wasn't punished. When I
asked why they didn't punish me, they thought I was ab-
normally good, or very conscientious, but the fact was I
wanted everything that was supposed to go with my conduct. As a young girl, foolish and inexperienced, my
mistakes never brought me to harm. In marriage at least
I expected to find reality; living with a man, I thought,
would bring home to me the mortal drama in which we
are supposed to be playing our parts; surely I should feel
it if the marriage turned out unhappy. But I was more
sheltered than ever—practically immune to life. It
wearied me to be complimented still on my good looks,
for the phrase was always a reason why they should cheat
me of what I wanted most. I understood what is meant
when men say beauty is a curse. Without sharp edges,
life is a smooth habit, and meaningless. I gave myself to
Paris because I loved him, but somewhere in my thoughts
was the hope that our love would actually be the great
tragedy it seemed to promise, and that in the end I should
suffer and feel. But my days in Troy might have been so
many seconds in a dream; no one took me seriously; no
one, not even Priam, upbraided me for ruining the city—

not even Hector, who on general principles disapproved
of Paris and me. When the end came, I said to myself,
I shall live at last, for Menelaos will surely kill me. Your
father will never know what was in my mind as I saw the
anger go out of his face, and that sheltering look come
back into it. It isn't exactly that he has forgiven me, but
I am not counted in the same world with other people—
I'm a sort of wraith. When he thinks of Paris and me,
and I'm not in his presence, he feels murderous, I believe;
but if I'm there when he remembers, he is, as you might
say, merely annoyed. Hermione, the reason I have such
a desire for life, the reason I want you to love life early,
is that I have never lived. But in my search for the real
things, I've learned to grasp at strict honesty with myself
and complete frankness about myself with other people;
it's my only hope. When you wished to save my reputation by saying I was in Egypt, never in Troy, don't you
see what you robbed me of? For all of us, I'm sure, in-
sincerity becomes a screen between life and our souls, but
it would be particularly dangerous for me. I am as far
away as I can get from the so-called respectable whose
respectability means only that they are afraid to live."

"I doubt if I am so beautiful," said Hermione, "that
I need follow your methods in order to make the acquaintance of sorrow. That's what you intimate, I suppose. But what has this to do with my choice of a husband?"

"You observed quite correctly," said Helen, "that my
advice differed from my conduct. I have been explaining
my conduct. Now let's come back to the advice. Or
rather, to your reasons for not liking Pyrrhus. You said
Orestes is your fate. I've expressed my opinion of that

theory, applied to Orestes or any one else. You also said, if I remember, that Pyrrhus is a brute. Just what did you mean?"

"He has bloody hands, I think. I don't care to marry a murderer."

"He was a terrible fighter, if that's what you mean," said Helen. "Do you prefer Orestes because he wasn't at the war?"

"Oh, no," said Hermione. "I mean that Pyrrhus killed Polyxena afterward. I know there was some story about his being obliged to offer her up on his father's tomb, for some good reason, but that sort of thing belongs to another age, as far as Orestes and I are concerned. It was plain murder, no matter how you explain it; it was no better than the sacrifice of Iphigeneia, when the fleet was sailing. When I think of your hero, that big strong man you praise to me, seizing a frail girl, dragging her to his distinguished father's tomb, bending back her head, and cutting her throat, as we do to the animals at a sacrifice—I hate him and everything about him. Do you think I could love him, and give myself up to his arms? I'd always think of that other girl, and wonder whether he'd like to make a pious offering of me. He killed Priam, too, they say—at the last moment, when the desperate old man tried to fight. A feeble dotard, who couldn't have harmed a child. Pyrrhus is a brute, and I rather think his father was too. Achilles liked to brain people, or cut them to pieces. Didn't he kill a girl once— the Amazon? Ran his spear right through her!"

"I've often thought of these killings," said Helen, "and with much the same horror as you express, but though there's evidently a good deal of wrong in it all, it's hard to know what is right. You say you can't bear to think of sacrificing a girl as we slay animals on the altars?"

"I certainly can't."

"But you don't object to sacrificing the animals?"

"Why should I? It's a ceremony—that's what they're for!"

"I dare say there are people," said Helen, "who shudder at the thought of drawing the knife across the throat of the poor sheep. Our religion is rather bloody, anyway, don't you think?"

"I see your argument," said Hermione; "you want me to say that the sacrifices aren't bloody, and then you'll say that Pyrrhus acted from a religious motive, and therefore he isn't brutal. Well, I really think our altars are barbarous—we should have outgrown them long ago, as we have outgrown human sacrifices."

"Many people feel that way," said Helen. "But if we kill the sheep for food, you have no prejudice against eating them, I know. If you consider meat for dinner a cannibalistic custom, you manage to hide your opinion."

"How foolish, mother! Of course we eat meat. Why shouldn't we?"

"The sheep might have an argument against it," said Helen, "but I have none. I merely wondered at what point you are at ease in the presence of what you call murder. I see. The animal slaughtered for religious purposes has your pity, but the one served up on your table fulfills its destiny as something for you to eat."

"I can't follow you when you are facetious. What am I to understand? Do you approve of human sacrifices? Do you think it was right to kill those two girls?"

"I wouldn't have killed them myself," said Helen, "yet in war men and women are sacrificed, in quite a religious sense, to the divine ends people think the war is serving. Whether it is good or bad for them to be sacrificed, I don't know. Nobody knows. But few object. If it is right to sacrifice people in war, I don't know what argument you could make against the altars. If you regret the sacrifice of those girls, you are regretting merely that they didn't exist for a few more years. You don't know what those extra years would have been like. If they were to be uneventful—I mean, inwardly so—if they were to be an unreal, unimportant number of breaths drawn, and meals eaten, and nights slept away, without any sense of living, then perhaps it was better for them to crowd many deep and strong emotions into a few hours. Don't think I'm against your humane tendencies, Hermione; I'm merely comparing the two girls you spoke of, sacrificed barbarously as they were, with myself, who have missed the excitements and the enthusiasms of life, as I just told you."

"You don't mean," said Hermione, "you wish Menelaos had killed you?"

"I was disappointed," said Helen. "No, I didn't want to die, but I did hope to know at least the terrors of life—and then your father became humane, as you perhaps think, and I knew there was nothing for it but years even less eventful than before, old age creeping up on our dull hearts—unless I could find a vital happiness in guiding you to a real life. I've said enough, and there's no use repeating it, but if you had my passion for living, all the greater because it has been thwarted, you'd take Pyrrhus, reckless and brutal as he seems, instead of that cautious and safe cousin of yours."

"You would, but I wouldn't, and I won't," said Hermione. "It isn't simply the killing. He has taken women home as slaves, and he has the old-fashioned idea of a hero's rights over the women he captures. They say Agamemnon brought Cassandra home, and you told me yourself you feared Clytemnestra would be jealous. Of course she would, though I'm sure Cassandra means nothing to my uncle. Orestes is sure she doesn't. But Pyrrhus is living with Andromache, Hector's widow, and probably with the other women he acquired at Troy. That's the kind of hero he is, and I say he's a brute and out of date. Orestes sees these things as I do; I fancy most people of our age feel the same way. I didn't realize how antiquated some of your notions are, mother, nor how conventional, until you began to urge Pyrrhus on me. I can just fancy myself as a further addition to his large herd—and my children playing cheerfully some day with Andromache's!"

"You are right again," said Helen—"partly right. The part you don't see, however, is the essence of the matter. I hesitate to answer you now, Hermione, for though I'm frank enough on any subject, there are things I'd rather not speak of unless to do so would be of service to you. This may well be the last time we discuss these questions; I've said all I could and told you all I know. Or almost all. I'll tell you the rest now. You'd like to have your man all to yourself. So would any woman who is in love—and men feel the same way about women. Love is very proprietary. But you go a step further, as I've noticed in others of your generation, and you want your man never to have cared for any one else. I dare say Orestes wouldn't feel sure of a wife who had pre-

viously lost her heart to another man. Now, that's all
nonsense. If the world is to act on that philosophy,
there's misery in store for lovers—all sorts of hypocrisy,
and dark secrets, and skeletons in the closet. It's your
notion of destined mates again, but in a sillier form. Of
course, when two people love each other—it's safer to
say, while they love—the rest of the race, for them, will
not exist; in that sense you ought to have your lover
quite to yourself. I should hate to see you married to
Pyrrhus unless you loved him passionately, and he you.
But let me tell you this, Hermione—the man who can
make a woman most happy is the one who could love
many women, who even has lived with several of them,
perhaps as Pyrrhus has done, and who at last devotes all
his love to her alone. By your theory, the best husband
ought to be the man who couldn't possibly have loved
before. Your theory is wrong. That kind of man, you'll
find, quite frequently is incapable of loving anybody very
much. . . . I suppose you think this wisdom of mine
immoral."

"I do," said Hermione.

II

"So do I," said Menelaos. "I heard that last speech of yours as I came in; in fact, I paused on the threshold, not to interrupt it. What sort of trash are you telling the child, Helen?"

"Truth, not trash," said Helen. "I didn't make the world."

"There was a lot in your love-of-life talk, a while ago, that escaped me," said Menelaos. "I begin to grasp it now. You think my loyalty to you is unmanly, an evidence of weakness. You admire men like Achilles and his precious son! Let me tell you this, dear wife—if I had loved you the way they love women, you wouldn't be here now. That night in Troy, I would have cut your throat!"

"There, Hermione, didn't I tell you?" said Helen. "You do begin to understand me, Menelaos, and as time goes on, I know you better. You didn't spare the woman you loved; you preserved me as an object of art!"

"I don't know why I spared you, but whatever the reason, you didn't deserve the kindness, and you don't appreciate it. As soon as my back is turned, you go plotting and planning to get your own way. I can't trust you. Didn't we make a bargain to have Pyrrhus here and let Hermione choose for herself? Now at the very moment when you know I'm distracted with worry, you get the child off to one side and try to settle the matter without me. Fortunately, she isn't likely to be persuaded by the kind of argument I heard. Very enticing prospect you held out, of a husband who might go in for polygamy at any minute. Hermione, my child, you may take my word for it, your mother has the recipe for excitement, but not for security."

"You missed the point, as usual," said Helen. "What you heard was not an argument necessarily in favor of Pyrrhus, neither was I trying to plead for the young man behind your back. Everything I've said might be interpreted in his favor, though if you had come earlier you would have been convinced that Hermione interprets everything against him. But I was trying to tell her a few things she ought to know about life—things she is not likely to learn from you. I shall continue to share with her what little knowledge I have, whether you are present or not. You would have been welcome, of course though I doubt if you would have been interested in what we were talking about. When I've said much the same things to you, a number of times, you have never paid attention. I'm not sure that Hermione has profited, either, from what I've told her."

"If I may judge of the rest by what I heard," said Menelaos, "you didn't tell her anything she could profit by. The implication I got was your usual one, that you hoped she'd be happier than you've been; and since your directions for picking out a husband don't correspond to any known portrait of me, I dare say you've made it fairly clear that you haven't been happy—not so happy as you would have been with Achilles or Pyrrhus. Is that a fair way to talk about your husband to your daughter?—I ask you, Helen—if you have a sense of fairness—is that decent or just?"

"My dear Menelaos," said Helen, "Hermione knows perfectly well that you and I have not been happy together; it only remains to explain why not. Did you think it would be good taste for me to pretend we were happy, after leaving you for so many years, and being brought back by force? Wasn't it reasonable to suppose that Hermione, who inherits your subtle mind, would suspect there was some unpleasantness between us? There are times, I should think, when even you, Menelaos, would prefer to face life as it is."

"There are times, Helen," said Menelaos. "Do you know, I think this is one of them! You've expressed your admiration for high-handed husbands once too often. Now I've an idea I'd like to play that part. What we agreed on about Pyrrhus, I'll abide by; when he comes, I'll entertain him; there'll be nothing said about matrimony. When he goes, Hermione will marry Orestes. And I'll listen to no more argument on the subject."

"Good!" said Helen. "That is practically what I wanted. My idea was to give Hermoine the liberty to choose her husband, after she had seen Pyrrhus, but I dare say she'll want to marry Orestes anyway, so your command will do no harm. If by a miracle she changes her mind and wants Pyrrhus, I understand that you will make her take Orestes anyway. Very well. Of course, that's being a high-handed parent, not a high-handed husband."

"I assume that Hermione wishes to marry Orestes," said Menelaos. "She understands I have no notion of compelling her to marry against her will."

"Oh, there you go, Menelaos," said Helen. "I knew you couldn't keep it up, but I did think you could pretend to be ferocious for more than three seconds. Why don't you put your foot down and say just who is to be our son-in-law? Tell Hermione to take him, tell him to take Hermione and no more words about it, and tell me to hold my tongue? Why don't you?"

"Your ridicule doesn't disturb me," said Menelaos. "I have put my foot down, as you will see. Hermione is to marry Orestes. I shall be civil to Pyrrhus—merely so. I don't like him, and I didn't like his father; now that you wish you had married one or both of them, I like them still less. While Pyrrhus is here, you may keep out of sight, except at meals, and at such other times as I shall specify. If you don't obey me, I'll have you locked in your room with a guard at the door. Pyrrhus will not think it strange, remembering your history. I'll tell him, with some of your frankness, that I would have treated you with more respect than you deserved, would have restored you to your old position in society, would have given back to you everything you threw away—but you wouldn't let me do it. You are an impossible case, Helen, good enough to look at on the outside, but inwardly anything but beautiful. You are a born trouble-maker. If I have to, I'll tell him the whole story."

"Menelaos," said Helen, "when you exhibit your conception of a strong man, I'm sorry for you. I really am sorry. You and your brother always quarreled with Achilles. You knew he was the bigger man, and you found excuses for annoying him. Now, having invited Pyrrhus to our house, at my request and for the special purpose we three understand—I include Hermione here—you say you will tell him all about me—you'll repeat, I suppose, some of the polite terms you employ in the bosom of the family. His visit, I can see, will be full of surprises for him, but on the whole he will enjoy it, for you will make clear how high you rate him and how little you think of yourself. You're quite right. If I must compare you two in brains, in appearance, in manners, in achievements—you'd better lock me up. Let Hermione see him; that's what I wanted in the first place. Besides, if you are to be present, I don't know that I wish to see Pyrrhus. I'd be too much ashamed of you, Menelaos. I couldn't explain why I married you, or why I came back. That is, of course, I could explain if the subject were once broached, but it would be impossibly bad form to discuss you with a guest."

"Why did you marry me, then," said Menelaos, "and why did you come back?"

"I made a mistake," said Helen.

"When I reflect," said Hermione, "that all this has been arranged for my happiness, I'm greatly puzzled. How do you two imagine I'm to profit in any way from this visit of Pyrrhus, when I know what you are thinking of him and of each other? If this is the preparation for making the right choice in marriage, I should say there must be less wear and tear in making the wrong choice and getting out of it later."

"You are quite right, Hermione," said Helen. "It is useless for Pyrrhus to come now. I'm sorry I made the suggestion in the first place. I meant well, but your father misinterprets my motives, and his mental attitude now is too deplorable for us to promise any guest a comfortable visit. I mean it, Menelaos; I give my consent to Orestes; I will raise no further objections, neither in your presence nor behind your back. And as a final favor

I ask you to recall the invitation—send word that Agamemnon is returned, and that business with him makes it necessary to postpone the pleasure we had suggested for ourselves."

"You don't get off so easily!" said Menelaos. "I see what you're after, clear enough; rather than have me tell the whole story, and let him report to the curious world what our relations are, you want to head him off before he gets here. I'll do nothing of the kind. Pyrrhus will come, if I can possibly persuade him to. If you value the liberty which is now yours, you will make no further objection to Orestes. And at the first opportunity Hermione will marry her cousin."

"Oh, father," said Hermione, "I wish you'd do as mother says—don't have Pyrrhus! Nobody wants him now—I'm sure you do mother an injustice—she spoke in the interest of our family peace. For herself, I really believe, she wouldn't mind your locking her up, and all that—it would give her the kind of excitement she yearns for. But this time she's thinking of me, of all of us, and her advice is good. I don't want that man here!"

"I'm sorry, but it's too late," said Menelaos, "I was forced to invite him, though I wanted him no more than you. Now he'll come."

"Menelaos," said Helen, "I doubt if you have the right to ask Pyrrhus here, in view of the heated arguments we've had, and the emotions that are running high in the family now. Some discourtesy might happen, and he take offense at it. He would think you were continuing your old feud with his father—people in general would think so—and your reputation would suffer."

"I'll take care of my reputation," said Menelaos.

"You're a fine one to advise me how to protect my name! Where did you learn the art?"

"You are uncivil," said Helen, "and you've lost your temper. I see with regret that your judgment has deserted you. Permit me to suggest that a failure to get on well with Pyrrhus would raise the question among our friends, whether there mightn't be something to say for previous guests of yours who didn't get on well with you. Even in the case of Paris, there were those who asked what you did to induce such a tragedy. You should be able to point to at least one young man who came to you as a guest and left as a friend. Since we can't be certain of such an end to this visit, I beg of you not to have Pyrrhus just now."

"The only negligence I contributed in the case of Paris," said Menelaos, "was that I trusted you out of my sight. I shan't do it again. Whether Pyrrhus leaves as a friend, I don't care a fig, but I guarantee he leaves this house alone. He won't take Hermione with him, and he won't take you. If you behave yourself, there'll be no quarrel with him."

"Have him come later, then," said Helen. "If he comes in the next few days, or even weeks, he may arrive just when you ought to go to your brother. Suppose Agamemnon sends for you in great haste; will you answer that you'd like to go to his rescue, but you have a guest with whom you don't dare trust your wife? If Agamemnon needs you, you'll have to go—you'd never forgive yourself if you didn't. And I really shouldn't care to be left with a guest here alone, knowing what your jealous suspicions would be for the rest of your life. It's best to keep yourself free for the possible emergency."

"My brother won't need me," said Menelaos. "The more I think of it, the surer I am. He can take care of Ægisthus, or if he wants help, Orestes is on the way."

"On the way where?" said Hermione. "How do you know that?"

"Why, Eteoneus got in touch with him, and lent him some weapons of mine, and he went off quite a while ago, to aid his father, if necessary."

"Oh, why didn't you go yourself to Agamemnon?" cried Hermione. "You could have done more good than Orestes; you have experience, and he's only—"

"If Orestes is fit for you to marry," said Helen, "he's not 'only'—he's a real man. He ought to go to his father—he's now where he belongs."

"I must say I believe that's right," said Menelaos. "though I thought of going myself too. But I sent a messenger to see if Agamemnon needs me; if he does, I'll go. Meanwhile I do think it's a favorable moment to learn what Orestes is made of; his behavior now will be more revealing than any number of conversations with your mother and me. . . . But my first impulse was to go, and your question leads me to consider again whether I wasn't right. I don't like to use my brother's danger as an experiment to test out his son. If I had obeyed my impulse, I'd be there now. Your mother advised me not to."

"I did advise you so," said Helen, "but you ought not to have taken my advice. At least, I thought less of you for taking it. Achilles would not have been so prudent, and I'm sure Pyrrhus wouldn't be. I advised you for your own safety—told you of danger and of possible ridicule—but what is that to a man who loves his brother, and who has the zest of life in him? I said you'd look foolish marching in with your troops, if Agamemnon and Clytemnestra had made it up. To another sort of man my argument would have suggested how welcome he and the troops would be if the quarrel were still on. No, Menelaos, you have your good points, but you can't play the part of a strong man, and everything you say and do confirms those truths I was trying to convey to Hermione. You've had two crises to face—one when I went off with Paris, the other when you knew your brother was coming home to great danger. You weren't equal to either. You had all the friends and neighbors in to help you at Troy, and now you're relying on Orestes. You did have some excuses in the first episode, but I don't see how you can forgive yourself now. Your brother may be in peril of his life, and at the very moment you are safe at home, hiding behind a door to hear what your wife is telling your daughter. Your wife happens to be advising the child to marry a real man if she can. You go into a rage at such transparent treachery, and threaten to lock your wife up if ever a real man comes into your home. This is the exhibition of yourself you have just made before Hermione. You have done more than I ever could to explain why my life has not been what she approves. In my heart I pity you, Menelaos; I look at you and think of the man I once loved, the character you were never willing to become. No woman could be so untrue to you as you have been to your own possibilities. Instead of being great, you have spent your days telling yourself you were, and exacting the respect you ought to have deserved. You have pursued the shadow. What I was telling Hermione should have made you go away from that door ashamed. If you had been man enough to kill me, that night in Troy, I never would have eloped with Paris. That's the whole story of your life and mine. If it wasn't revenge you were after, then you had no excuse for involving so many people and ruining Troy; you could have forgiven me single-handed. When I speak of strong men, it's not physical strength alone I mean. You could have been very strong over my eloping, and yet not lifted a finger—that is, if you had been disposed to use your mind, and if you had had a strong mind. I can imagine a certain type of man, in your situation, saying boldly that he had bribed Paris to relieve him of an obnoxious wife—that he had had to pay him well—that he had gone away deliberately, to make it easy—that the furniture hadn't been stolen, it had been thrown in. A bold statement of that sort would have ruined Paris, and I admit it would have finished me. But in that case you would have been committed to give me up forever. You couldn't do that, could you, Menelaos? You wanted to brand me as an outcast, and at the same time recover me for your wife. I pity you. It's too late now to play the rough hero; you will simply remember how weak you were, and try to atone to yourself for the memory by nagging at me, by eavesdropping, by opposing my best plans for Hermione's welfare. Whether you liked Achilles or not, can't you be honest about him, and recognize the contrast between you two? Can't you see that he was disinterested at Troy, until you and Agamemnon picked a quarrel with him? How clear his character is! It isn't surprising that I admire him; the terrible thing is that you don't."

"Then you think I ought to go to Agamemnon," said Menelaos.

"I advised you not to go," said Helen.

"Why not?"

"You remember perfectly well—it is dangerous to go, and there is a chance that you'll make yourself ridiculous."

"You think that Achilles, or some fellow like him, would go even if advised against it?"

"There are a few things for each of us, Menelaos, in which we can take no advice. No woman could have advised Achilles about danger—for him it didn't exist. And it would never occur to Achilles—nor to any one else—that he could be ridiculous."

"I'll go to my brother," said Menelaos. "It's not too late to be myself, as you say."

"There's some one at the door," said Hermione.

"Who's at the door?" said Menelaos. "Come in! Oh, it's you, Eteoneus. Why didn't you knock? This is a private conversation, and I don't like eavesdropping."

"I HESITATED to come in," said Eteoneus. "I didn't want to come at all."

"What's the matter?" said Menelaos.

"We have news," said Eteoneus, "and I don't like to tell it."

"Tell us, Eteoneus," said Helen; "don't keep us waiting. We can stand the news, good or bad!"

"Agamemnon is dead," said Eteoneus.

"Menelaos!" cried Helen. She went over to him, and stood by his side.

"My brother is dead!" repeated Menelaos.

"I didn't like to tell you," said Eteoneus.

"Who—how did he die?" asked Menelaos.

"He was killed," said Eteoneus. "Ægisthus killed him."

"Never!" said Menelaos. "It's a mistake. Ægisthus couldn't stand a moment before my brother in a fair fight!"

"No, he couldn't," said Eteoneus, "but it wasn't a fair fight. Agamemnon went into his house, as the trader reported to us, and thinking himself safe at home, he took off his armor and hung up his sword. Then they killed him."

"They? Who were they?" cried Helen.

"I didn't like to bring this news," said Eteoneus. "If there had been any one else to send, I'd have stayed out at the gate."

"Tell us all," said Menelaos. "Who killed my brother?"

"I believe Ægisthus was most to blame," said Eteoneus; "he's the one Orestes is after now, and it may be he has already paid him back for it. The messenger says Clytemnestra was implicated."

"My sister, my sister! I knew it!" cried Helen.

"Knew what, Helen?" said Menelaos.

"I knew in my heart she would murder him some day. She's the one, not Ægisthus! Eteoneus is trying to spare me, but I'm sure that's the fact."

"Helen," said Menelaos, "you and I have had difficult moments, and I've said hard things about you, to your face, but I don't believe a sister of yours would do that. I can't believe it of a woman so near to us, of your blood. This murder is just the sneaking kind of thing a coward like Ægisthus would plan. If Clytemnestra had been the leader, the killing would have been bold and dramatic. I can imagine her doing it in the open and boasting about it, but not springing this dastardly trap. My brother! He said we should never see each other again!"

"I think father is right," said Hermione. "My aunt is given to a fearful temper, at all times, but when she is angry, as she was with Agamemnon, she is a downright fury, Orestes says. This secret murder wouldn't appeal to her; it would conceal the justice of her cause. If she had thought of killing Agamemnon, it would have been by way of a public execution; she did consider him the murderer of her child, and he really was that, wasn't he? But stabbing him in the back wouldn't make her case any stronger."

"There was something in Clytemnestra's character I never understood," said Helen, "and never trusted. She was rather sentimental, and you might think she was soft but underneath I always had an unpleasant conviction she was inhuman. I'd give everything to know she did not murder Agamemnon, but I'm perfectly sure she did."

"If she had done it," said Menelaos, "the people would have killed her in revenge before this. My brother was never what you could call popular, but his men were devoted to him, and they must have been around him at the time. It's fairly clear to me that Ægisthus set the snare and now the story is afloat that Clytemnestra helped. That's the effect of her improper life with him; people will naturally think she planned it."

"There's another thing too," said Hermione. "Clytemnestra knows there will be some sort of revenge for this murder. Orestes will exact a terrible penalty from Ægisthus, but if Clytemnestra were implicated, he would have to punish her too—all the murderers, in fact. She understands where such a deed would end."

"Orestes wouldn't kill his mother," said Menelaos "otherwise I agree with your argument. I think Helen is unjust to her sister. . . . Eteoneus, did the messenger give you any further details?"

"I haven't told you the details yet," said Eteoneus "I gave you a mere outline."

"Then there's more?" said Helen.

"There are the details," said Eteoneus. "The messenger says Agamemnon went into the house, as the trader reported, and after a while the people went away not seeing more entertainment in prospect. Then Clytemnestra had them all called back, and she came out and made them a speech. She said she had enjoyed such admirable relations with her neighbors that there was no reason why she should not take them into her complete confidence. She had, she said, just killed her husband. They probably knew that Ægisthus and she had been living together, and considered themselves man and wife in the eyes of the gods, if the gods had noticed it. She had doubted that Agamemnon would return—rather hoped he wouldn't, for he had murdered their daughter, and she was bound by every pious obligation, as they would readily appreciate, to slay the murderer of her child. She wished it understood that she had killed Agamemnon to avenge Iphigeneia, not in order to pursue her love for Ægisthus; that love, in fact, had come about of itself as an indirect consequence of what Agamemnon had done. She confessed that the duty to avenge her child had been complicated by the fact that he was her legal husband, and she had once loved him. She confessed also that he had entirely solved her scruples by the manner of his return; he had actually brought Cassandra home to be his concubine. She had therefore drawn him into a remote part of the house, had invited him to rest, and when his armor was removed, had killed him. In a burst of jealousy, which she mentioned with regret, she had also killed Cassandra. It was clear now, she said, that this second murder was unnecessary, but it's hard to think of everything at the time. She wished them all to know, first, that she had done it herself, without aid from anybody; and secondly, that she was proud of it and had nothing to apologize for. She would now take Ægisthus as her lawful second husband; she had accepted no aid from him in killing Agamemnon, for after

all, the feud had to do with her daughter and not with
her love-affairs. Ægisthus was entirely innocent. If
anybody was guilty, she was, but she was inclined to
think the episode wiped out guilt instead of incurring it.
The messenger considered it quite a speech," said Eteoneus, "and at first it was well received, but the people
began to notice, as they thought it over, that she really
was shielding Ægisthus, and trying to lay the blame
where no vengeance could strike. The messenger says
that Orestes will have the people with him if he suc-
ceeds in killing Ægisthus, but if he fails, they'll probably
stand by Clytemnestra—she has the situation well in
hand."

"Of course she has," said Helen. "She undoubtedly
planned it all, even the speech, long ago. She leaves
nothing to accident. She murdered him. I'm glad at
least she didn't pretend otherwise."

"I can't believe it, not even now," said Menelaos.
"Why, it's far worse than I thought!"

"Or I," said Helen, "but I was prepared for whatever
Clytemnestra might do. I grieve for you, Menelaos, and
for myself; I feel as though the blame for my family's
wrong-doing ought to fall on me. . . . If she simply
wanted to live with Ægisthus, she could have gone off
with him and left Agamemnon to himself. But to sit
there at home, and eat his food, and consume his property, with that good-for-nothing Ægisthus sharing it
all—and then when Agamemnon came back, to pretend
an affectionate welcome, get him off his guard, and then
stab him—well, that's Clytemnestra."

"I'm amazed you are so hard on your own sister,"
said Menelaos. "I feel that way, of course, but I rather
should have expected you to defend her."

"I have my own reasons," said Helen.

"Eteoneus," said Hermione, "do you think Orestes can handle Ægisthus alone?"

"I asked the messenger about that," said Eteoneus, "but he had no opinion. Not much is known about Ægisthus. He may be a weak sort of person, as he seems, the sentimental shadow of Clytemnestra, or he may be the brains and the cause of the whole thing. It's very hard to say."

"Don't you think you'd better go help him, father?" said Hermione.

"I'm going within the hour—I made up my mind to that while we were talking," said Menelaos.

"Where are you going?" said Helen.

"I'm going to help Orestes have his vengeance on Ægisthus."

"And on Clytemnestra?"

"Dear me, no!" said Menelaos. "We'll leave her to her guilty conscience. But Ægisthus is the villain, I do believe, all the more because she defended him so energetically. We'll see that he pays for it. I'll be back at once, in time for Pyrrhus."

"Bring Orestes back with you," said Helen, "and the wedding can take place without further delay. It will rehabilitate that branch of the family, socially I mean, to have the alliance with your daughter, and it will take the poor fellow's mind off his terrible troubles."

"That wedding can wait," said Menelaos.

"Of course it can," said Helen. "Meanwhile, what will you do if you meet Clytemnestra now? Won't it be rather awkward for you to pass the time of day while you're killing her lover? And won't it be still more awkward afterward? You ought to consider every side of it, Menelaos. This time I'm not urging you to avoid danger or ridicule; I'm thinking that since Agamemnon is gone, you must approach Clytemnestra, as the surviving parent, when you arrange the details of Hermione's wedding, and perhaps it would therefore be wiser to keep out of this feud—especially since Orestes seems able to bear her wrath."

"I don't see that at all," said Hermione. "He can't keep out of the feud, mother; he can't talk to Clytemnestra about me, nor about anything else, without remembering who killed Agamemnon. He might just as well go now and help Orestes, and I can marry without Clytemnestra's approval—no arrangements need be made with her. In fact, I don't wish her approval. I intend to have nothing to do with her."

"You can't ignore your mother-in-law," said Menelaos. "I'm glad you feel about her as you do, but it will be difficult for you to get on after you have given yourself to her son. Do you know, Hermione, it might be wise to reconsider the whole situation. I like Orestes better than ever, and all that sort of thing, but in marriage you have to reckon with the relatives. Marriage is a frightfully social institution. I have absolutely no social leanings toward Clytemnestra."

"Father; are you going back on me, and on Orestes?" said Hermione.

"Of course I'm not," said Menelaos, "but you can see for yourself how it is. I could have arranged the marriage with Agamemnon, and swallowed my prejudice against his wife, but now the wife is the head of the house. That's a very different matter. I can't take steps to marry my daughter to the son of my brother's murderer!"

"To the son of your brother!" said Hermione.

"That's all very well," said Menelaos, "but I'm considering the other side of him. Suppose we let the whole subject drop for a while; Orestes is preoccupied, anyway, and there's no hurry."

"I can't let Orestes drop, if that's what you mean," said Hermoine. "I'm committed to him—I'm engaged—I've promised myself. I haven't changed my mind in any respect. When he's ready to take me, I'm his. I thought you knew that, father. I'd like to marry with your blessing, but I shall marry Orestes. I wish you'd help with Ægisthus—but he can probably manage by himself."

"I don't think that's quite dutiful," said Menelaos. "You ought to listen to a parent's advice. We used to respect our elders."

"I respect your elders too," said Hermione, "but you are breaking faith with me, just because Clytemnestra killed Agamemnon. Mother has won you over, without your knowing it. She and her family would spoil my life, if I let them."

"Hermione," said Helen, "that's not the way to speak to your father. He's quite right—you should be respectful toward your parents. The question isn't whether they deserve the courtesy—nobody made you a judge of that; the question is whether your own nature is fine enough to prefer courteous expression. . . . And I'd like to remind you that you have my full permission to marry Orestes. I pleaded with you merely to see Pyrrhus; even about that I grew lukewarm. Marry Orestes when you like, so far as I'm concerned; it's for you and your father to work out."

"The only way I'll work it out," said Menelaos, "is to postpone the whole matter. I'll go now and do what I can to help the boy; after that we'll see."

"You may wait, as you say," said Hermione, "but it's only frank of me to repeat that I've nothing to gain by waiting. I've made up my mind, and I feel I belong to Orestes all the more because of the trouble he's in."

"Oh, Hermione, can't you have some sense?" said Helen. "Your father will help Orestes now, and afterward, just because of that help, the wedding will follow quite naturally. If you only wait, you'll see."

"She won't see anything of the kind!" said Menelaos—"not necessarily. The relations are distinct. If I thought they weren't, I'd let Orestes handle the whole thing himself! He'd better not think I'm committed to him for life, as Hermione says she is, just because I join him now to avenge my brother's murder!"

IV

"You don't think he will?" said Hermione.

"I'm sure he won't," said Eteoneus.

"I don't like to think my father a coward," said Hermione, "but it will be difficult to explain his staying home now. It's not only his nephew who needs him; the murdered man is his own brother, and decency requires him to see justice done."

"He's no coward, not in the ordinary sense," said Eteoneus. "Your mother dissuaded him. You heard her do it. When she began urging him to go help Orestes, so that he could arrange the sooner for your wedding, and when she reminded him that he'd have to arrange the wedding details with Clytemnestra, I knew there'd be no helping Orestes, and no wedding. I'm not one of your mother's devoted worshipers—first and last I'm your father's man—but you have to admit she's clever."

"That's no reason why father should not go. He knows I can arrange the marriage without his help; he can ignore Clytemnestra, if he prefers."

"I wonder if he can ignore her in this revenge," said Eteoneus. "Didn't you think your mother and your father were evading that aspect of the case? It was half mentioned, but they didn't follow it up. In justice Clytemnestra ought to be punished for murdering her husband. Your mother doesn't wish to plead for her sister, or seem to plead, but naturally she doesn't want her own husband to kill her sister. It's quite a situation. Orestes certainly won't kill his mother, so if anybody is to take vengeance on her, it must be Menelaos. What kind of mess would it be if he came home and told us that the ghost of Agamemnon had been properly satisfied by the blood of his murderers, Clytemnestra and Ægisthus? Do you think he and Helen could sit down comfortably to their dinner, after that, and talk about the news of the house since he went away? Helen says severe things of her sister, but Menelaos knows he had better not lift his hand against Clytemnestra."

"Eteoneus, do you think Orestes is strong enough to meet Ægisthus?"

"Alone, yes; but if Clytemnestra is helping her lover, Orestes should be careful. The combination was too much for Agamemnon. That's another reason why Menelaos will stay here, I think. Even if they leave Clytemnestra alone, she's not likely to repay them by keeping out of the quarrel; no doubt she'd be glad to stick a knife into your father, if he came with any unkind designs on Ægisthus. They ought to cut her throat first, and do for Ægisthus afterward."

"How bloody-minded you are, Eteoneus!" said Hermione. "You could have been another Pyrrhus, if you had given your attention to it."

"I suspect you mean no compliment," said Eteoneus. "What's the trouble with Pyrrhus?"

"He's a brute," said Hermione. "He doesn't mind killing women, not a bit; in fact, if he were in Orestes' place, I dare say he'd rather kill Clytemnestra and let Ægisthus go free."

"There's something to be said for that point of view; she's the guilty one," said Eteoneus, "and she's a woman."

"Just the reason for sparing her," said Hermione.

"I know," said Eteoneus, "that's the last word in fine manners, but I don't believe in it. Women make most of the trouble in the world, and it's weakness, I say, to spare them their punishment. Otherwise they'd always be doing as they liked."

"You are talking nonsense, Eteoneus, and you know better. Woman's life is a succession of trouble and sorrows. It's hard enough just to be a woman, but men make her lot infinitely wretched."

"I don't see that at all," said Eteoneus. "As far as I've been able to observe, the women like the men and all their ways; they like men to be brutes; they help make them so. When a woman tells me she has a hard lot, I say, 'Haven't you, though!' or something like that, and we're both satisfied. It's a fiction."

"You don't mean it's a fiction that Pyrrhus treated Polyxena badly when he sacrificed her on his father's tomb?"

"No worse than he treated the men he killed in the sack of Troy."

"But they could defend themselves!"

"So could she."

"Women are defenseless before men," said Hermione.

"Are they!" said Eteoneus. "Clytemnestra!"

"That's a special case, and it's not what I'm talking about," said Hermione.

"It's the most recent case," said Eteoneus, "and it's not without precedent. All women are trouble-makers."

"I wonder if Andromache thinks so," said Hermione. "Pyrrhus carried her home with him, his slave, and the woman who had been Hector's wife was forced to put up with the brutal caresses of that murderer. They say she's going to have a child."

"Does Andromache say his caresses are brutal?" asked Eteoneus. "If that's an important question with you, you ought to ask her. You really should not talk about him until you have made inquiries. How do you know she doesn't like him? You say you don't want to marry Pyrrhus because he has treated Andromache badly. You don't seem to know much of women, Hermione, and I dare say you are as ignorant of men. The real reason why you shouldn't marry Pyrrhus is that Andromache would be jealous of you; she would probably treat you as Clytemnestra did Cassandra."

"You don't know any more about Andromache than I do," said Hermione, "but assuming that you are right, I repeat what I said, that women in general have a hard time, and that men treat us so badly we lose our respect for them."

"It can't be done," said Eteoneus. "You can't treat a woman so badly as to lose her respect—that is, provided you still show some sort of interest in her."

"Then I suppose you think a woman is happy, perhaps even deeply complimented, if one of your precious sex makes love to her, and betrays her, and deserts her. That sort of thing composes the tragic story of many women, no matter how you men choose to shut your eyes to it."

"I suppose they generally don't like to be deserted," said Eteoneus—"that is, so long as they like the man; when they grow tired of him, he can't desert too soon. But generally, as I said, you women like attention. As to the other parts of the tragedy you sketch, it's all bosh,

Hermione. Women aren't seduced. I know what I'm talking about. They want the men and the men want them. They both get what they want, and as far as I can see, the men get the worst of it."

"I'd no idea you were such a woman-hater," said Hermione. "So hard in your emotions! I thought experience brought more tenderness."

"I'm no woman-hater," said Eteoneus. "I simply happen to have some of that experience you speak of. You can't tell me much about women."

"You've never been married, I believe," said Hermione.

"Do you interpret that fact to mean I don't know anything about women?" said Eteoneus. "It's the proof of my wisdom."

"Oh, that's all very well for a joke, Eteoneus, but the fact that you've avoided my sex doesn't prove you understand their feelings, their sufferings under the treatment they receive from men."

"I suppose I'll have to speak plainly if I'm to get anywhere in this argument," said Eteoneus, "and I'm not sure you'll like me any better after I've spoken, but the fact is, Hermione, I belong to the older and tougher generation which you despise; my manners before age reduced me to gate-keeping were quite correct by the standards of our time, but they would seem to you—what was your word?—brutal. I haven't avoided women. You misunderstood me; I avoided marriage."

Oh!" said Hermione. . . . "I'm sorry to say there are still a number of men who lead that sort of life."

"Yes, a number of men," said Eteoneus, "and several women in your family."

"Don't you think it's wrong?" said Hermione. "I always supposed you didn't approve of my mother's conduct."

"Certainly not," said Eteoneus. "All irregularities should be punished, if society is to last, but it's natural to do it, after all. I tell you, Hermione, your mother's running away didn't surprise me much; women will do anything. What got me was your father's forgiving her."

"Did you think this way in your young wild days," said Hermione, "when you were teaching girls to do wrong?"

"Fiddlesticks," said Eteoneus, "you can't teach women anything. Yes, I always thought this way. Wrong is wrong, but some of it is natural. I ought to have been punished, I dare say. I wasn't. It would have been worth it."

"I mustn't listen to such talk," said Hermione. "I knew there were men who thought as you do, but I never met one before. You make me feel creepy all over. Here I've known you since I was born, and you've been so careful of us all, yet you believe in such immoral things! I didn't suspect it."

"Watching this family in recent years has made me think a lot," said Eteoneus, "about morality. Before that, I took the world for granted, and did what other men did—the ones I admired. I must say I can't see that the modern ways are very different, or come to more satisfactory ends. I go on the principle that women are still what they were in my time—and men too. I'm sorry people try to understand them by new theories. Now, you say I'm immoral, and it makes you creepy all over to hear

me. Perhaps. But I rather think you were interested, or
you wouldn't have stayed to listen. That's the way women
used to be. You know how we always did after a fight,
when we had captured a town. Your generation think
it's not civilized, but it was the correct thing when I was
young, and no one complained. We'd kill the men, and
then we'd take the women. Most of the women I've
known, I met on such occasions. You think that kind of
adventure is cruel to the women, don't you? Well, I
never had a girl that way who seemed to mind it very
much; the protests were merely formal. They'd run away
from you, and you'd catch them, and carry them off to
some quiet place, and—well, that's all there was to it. I
can't see that marriage is different, except in the length
of the courtship. And it's perfectly fair in war, as we
used to go about it; the women knew in advance what
would happen to them if their side got beaten—they'd be
married to a stranger, but he'd be the better man. Now
Achilles and some of the youngsters behave differently,
I'm told; Chryseis was a captive, but he had nothing to do
with her. He had the right to do as he liked, of course,
but I don't see any particular advantage in such conduct.
Pyrrhus and Agamemnon have the old-fashioned point of
view. Agamemnon was a great man. He made only one
mistake."

"Why, Eteoneus, according to your principles Paris
was right!"

"I won't say he was wrong," said Eteoneus, "if he
wanted to take so desperate a risk. They killed him, you
remember. The whole episode would have been managed
no differently in my day, except that your mother would
not have returned."

"You don't mean you would have had my father kill her?"

"Well, that kind of thing has been done," said Eteoneus. "Of course it is embarrassing to discuss the theory specifically with your mother here. I'm far from plotting to kill her now, though I'm still thrown out a bit whenever I see her—it's like living with a dead person."

"See here, Eteoneus—you wouldn't have Orestes or my father kill Clytemnestra?"

"Certainly not Orestes; that would be impious, to kill his own mother. If it were his wife, that would be another thing. Agamemnon ought to have killed her. That was his mistake. She was faithless."

"How about the men who are faithless?" said Hermione. "You confess to having led what I should call a bad and a cruel life, and you never reformed; you simply became too old to misbehave. Why wouldn't it have been proper for some woman whom you had deserted to kill you? This faithfulness shouldn't be all on one side."

"That was Clytemnestra's idea," said Eteoneus. "That woman is strangely modern, considering her age."

"Age!" said Hermione. "You are tottering into the grave, Eteoneus, with the beastliest set of ideas I've ever heard. If you are like Pyrrhus, my worst fears of him are confirmed. I'm glad I belong to another generation!"

V

"I've come to see Helen," said Charitas.

"She's not at home," said Eteoneus. "Is there a message you'd like to leave for her?"

"Not at home!" said Charitas. "Is she ever at home? I wanted to see her personally. Are you sure she's out? She hasn't been in once when I've called. I must say it looks rather pointed."

"She's certainly not at home now. She'll be sorry to have missed you."

"I'd like to be sure she will," said Charitas. "Your mistress doesn't treat her old friends at all well."

"She'll be sorry to hear you think so," said Eteoneus. "I'll give her your message as soon as she comes in."

"Do nothing of the kind! I have the highest regard for her, or I should not be here. But I don't like to feel I wasted my time in coming over. The news about poor Agamemnon just reached us, and I wanted to show her there was no change in my attitude, no matter what happened in her family. At such a time she ought to be at home, one would think. I suppose she has got a sort of habit of being away. Do you notice that about her?"

"It's too bad you had the walk for nothing," said Eteoneus. "She'll appreciate your thoughtfulness. Lately she has been much occupied."

"Who wouldn't be, with such terrible things happening, one right after the other! I suppose the family sides with Agamemnon?"

"Well, Agamemnon's dead," said Eteoneus. "I don't know what you mean by siding with him."

"Why, he and Clytemnestra quarreled, didn't they?"

"I never heard that they exchanged a single unpleasant word," said Eteoneus. "A man can die, you know, without quarreling with his wife."

"You know what I mean—Clytemnestra was unfaithful to him."

"Oh, that!" said Eteoneus. "Yes, I know about that, but I doubt if he did. His death was so sudden, she probably didn't have time to tell him."

"He must have know !" said Charitas. "What I heard was that he tried to kill her, and quite right too, but she called so loud, Ægis hus came to the rescue, and together they murdered Agamemnon."

"That's quite a story, if it were only true," said Eteoneus. "Who told you that?"

"It came indirectly from this house—one of your servants and one of mine," said Charitas. "I hoped to get the facts from Helen."

"As soon as she comes in," said Eteoneus, "I'll tell her you want to know whether Agamemnon tried to kill her sister first, or whether her sister just up and killed Agamemnon."

"Oh, is that the way it happened? I hadn't heard that version. Who brought the report, Eteoneus?"

"I believe some other friends stopped in to call, earlier in the day. The only thing we know is that Agamemnon died shortly after his return."

"He must have known how she was behaving, and he had a fierce temper when he was roused, hadn't he?"

"Well, I don't know," said Eteoneus. "I never tried

to find out, when he used to come here. He was a very remarkable man, I always thought. His wife was remarkable too, for more than her good looks."

"Yes," said Charitas, "many thought her much more beautiful than Helen. The difference between them, all their lives, illustrates how accidental fame and success are. Every one has heard of Helen's beauty; few know about Clytemnestra. Helen lived a most scandalous life with another man, and her husband has taken her back— isn't it odd?—and Clytemnestra's misbehavior has led to murder. . . . You think she didn't kill him in self-defense?"

"There's a good deal to be said for self-defense," said Eteoneus, "only I don't know that any one attacked her, and I didn't say she killed Agamemnon. He's dead That's what I said. Was there any other message you wished to leave for Helen?"

"I haven't left any message yet," said Charitas. "Tell her I called, of course. . . . Eteoneus, don't you think Menelaos and his brother had queer notions about their wives?"

"They had exceptional wives," said Eteoneus, "but I don't know which of their notions you refer to."

"They were strangely gullible, that's what I mean. You seem to think, and I'm sure no one knows better than you do, that Agamemnon came home unsuspecting. The idea!"

"Oh, there's nothing to wonder at; wives and husbands really know little about each other when they're at home, and they lose track completely when one of them's away. You, for instance, don't know whether your husband's faithful to you."

"How dare you, Eteoneus! I shall speak to Mene-laos—you have forgotten your place. My husband is altogether faithful."

"I'm ready to believe he is," said Eteoneus. "I certainly don't want you to go home and murder him because of my remark. Of course he's faithful. I was only pointing out that you don't know whether he is or not. You ought to understand how it was with Agamemnon. He thought his wife was better than she was. It's a common mistake."

"I don't know why I talk to you, Eteoneus—you are discourteous and presuming. I came over just to—"

"Helen will be sorry she was not at home," said Eteoneus. "May I send one of the girls back with a sunshade for you? It's warm walking."

"Oh, Eteoneus, perhaps you can tell me—what sort of person is this Adraste, who goes around with Helen?"

"She's Helen's personal servant, and a fine young woman, I'll say. Helen likes them beautiful."

"I mean, what sort of character, of course. Any one can see the child's good-looking. Is she trustworthy and safe—with men, I mean?"

"Safe!" said Eteoneus. "I should say not. She'll probably break more hearts than any one you ever knew—after Helen herself. I'm very fond of her; she's a general favorite, even with us old folks. Your son thinks well of her—he could give you a more intimate account of her than I can."

"You tell me the worst! That's what I feared, Eteoneus. I can't have my boy in love with that girl! I can't!"

"Well, it's happened without your aid," said Eteoneus.

"He's in love with her, and she with him, and mighty lucky for him too; he won't find another girl as fine who will have him."

"Why, she's no better than a servant!" said Charitas.

"Well, he's not even that," said Eteoneus. "He's a nice boy, but entirely useless, so far, and the best thing I know about him is that she thinks well of him. What are you worrying about? Let them be happy."

"I'm sure she'll get him into trouble," said Charitas. "He is without experience, and she hasn't lived with Helen for nothing; she'll have designs on him."

"I've seen a good deal of wickedness in my time," said Eteoneus, "and some think I had my share in it, but I don't know enough about deviltry to understand how that girl could get your boy into trouble. If I were responsible for her, I might fear your boy, but she can't do him any harm."

"Yes, she can," said Charitas, "she can ruin his career—she can marry him."

"There's something in that," said Eteoneus, "and yet, marriage isn't necessarily fatal. He'll take after his father and be a docile husband, and with such a wife he'll have every reason to be."

"You speak as though the whole affair were settled."

"It ought to be settled soon," said Eteoneus. "The gossip around the house is that they consider themselves man and wife, and when two young people in love begin to feel that way toward each other, it's practically settled."

"Do you mean they are living together now?"

"I couldn't prove it," said Eteoneus, "but that's what I think, and we all approve—that is, we feel that Damastor has won him a fine wife."

"He has, has he? You do, do you? She'll never lay eyes on him again! I'll see to that before this day is over. I'll send that boy to a safe place till he's cured. I knew from the first what would happen if Helen were allowed to do as she chose! Menelaos has a lot to answer for! Of all the wicked things—to entice such a boy into a house like this!"

"See here, that's strong talk, if you know what you're saying!" said Eteoneus. "Nobody enticed your son over here. I couldn't keep him out, though Helen told me to. And it seems to me you'll do a pretty mean thing if you separate them now. The boy made love to her and won her, and perhaps it's just the time when he shouldn't desert her. It wouldn't be decent of him."

"The airs you people put on in this house, talking to me of decency!" said Charitas. "Was it decent of Helen to bring that girl to my home, and send her off to talk to him at the end of the garden? That's what she did— that's where it began, right under my eyes! Was it decent—"

"If you saw their love begin, on your own premises and right under your eyes," said Eteoneus, "you must have known about it all along, and you ought to share the responsibility with your boy for anything he's done. This house is all it should be—now. I'm too old-fashioned to like what happened a while back, but I'll stand by the house, in all the essentials. The young people fall in love now-a-days, just as they used to do, and some of the old people have forgotten what it's about. If you take that boy away now, I'll say you're the meanest woman I've met in a long life, and I've met all kinds!"

"This time you've gone too far," said Charitas. "When

my husband hears how you've spoken to me, he will have a word with Menelaos."

"He will if I let him in," said Eteoneus, "or he can learn from his son how to sneak in the back way, through the servants' quarters!"

PART FOUR
DEATH AND BIRTH

DEATH AND BIRTH

I

"CHARITAS sent her husband to complain of the way you spoke to her, Eteoneus," said Menelaos. "I'm sorry to say it's not the only criticism of you that has come to my attention in the last few days. At this crisis, when you know how heavily burdened I am already, it does seem as though you might refrain from questionable ventures in deportment. I said I wanted to speak with you, but now that you are here, I don't know what to say. You've been my servant for many years. You were the one person in the household I used to count on for absolute propriety. But in recent months your tongue has been getting you into trouble. You yourself reported some high words with Orestes, and I had to object to your disposition to discuss my wife. Now our best neighbor comes in and it's his wife you've discussed. What has happened, Eteoneus? And what ought I to do with you?"

"Nothing has happened to me, Menelaos," said the gate-keeper; "nothing but old age. I believe age has not essentially altered my character, but if you think it has, perhaps you ought to retire me. In the days when my conduct gave satisfaction, only the common run of travelers stood outside your door, and only normal events happened inside of it. Now, as you'll admit, we have strange

visitors, and we receive strange messages, and what
goes on inside this house is new, or ought to be new, to
my experience. I doubt if my speech has become less
guarded; I should probably have made the same com-
ments forty years ago, if the same events had happened
then."

"I don't like you to mention your age," said Menelaos,
"and I don't care to consider your retiring. I know perfectly well I couldn't replace you in your present office.
The younger servants are only servants now—they feel
no family ties. But no matter how much I need you, and
how much I think of you, you must see what a fix I'm in
when complaints are made. People have criticized my
house too much already. My brother's death will make
more talk. If I didn't esteem you so highly, I'd send you
off without a moment's hesitation. Instead, I ask you,
man to man, what you'd do if you were in my place."

"Well, if I were in your place," said Eteoneus, "I'd
begin by stating the precise nature of the complaint
Charitas made to you."

"Her husband, not Charitas," said Menelaos.

"Oh, I understand," said the gate-keeper.

"He says you insulted his wife when she came to call
on Helen. First, you wouldn't let her in. Then you answered her questions rather sarcastically. For a climax,
you told her she was the meanest woman you had ever
met, and you thought you had met the extreme ex-
amples."

"That's nearer the truth than you'd expect from an
angry woman," said Eteoneus, "especially getting it from
you, who had it from her husband, who knew nothing
about it, except what she told him. She asked if Helen

was at home. I said she wasn't. That's what she means by my not letting her in. She's right, practically. Helen told me to say she was not at home, if any one called, but she also told me to see that Charitas didn't get across the threshold, and Charitas suspects something of the kind. She said Helen's consistent absence was beginning to seem pointed. I was doing what I was commanded to do, Menelaos, and I did it all the more conscientiously because I'm no great admirer of your wife, and her orders give no pleasure."

"If Helen didn't wish to see Charitas," said Menelaos, "you certainly should not be blamed. But why didn't Helen want to see her—did she give a reason?"

"Yes," said Eteoneus, "she said she couldn't bear to discuss the death of your brother, and her sister's part in it, with curious neighbors, and she was sure Charitas would be on hand promptly as soon as the rumor spread."

"Hm!" said Menelaos. "Her feelings of reticence do her credit. She seems to know Charitas."

"She knows her sex. I doubt if she'd see Charitas, anyway," said Eteoneus. "My opinion is, she looks on the murder as the most plausible excuse she's had in a long time for keeping Charitas out. She has given me the same orders before, with other reasons. This one's by far the best."

"I wonder what has happened between them," said Menelaos. "They used to be friends, and Charitas is the kind of woman I like to have Helen associated with—very steady, sensible, thoroughly reliable."

"She never told me her opinion of Charitas," said the gate-keeper, "but I doubt if she thinks her either sensible or reliable."

"What does she think her?"

"She said once that Charitas was respectable."

"At least!" said Menelaos.

"She meant it as no compliment," said Eteoneus. "She meant that Charitas sticks to the conventions."

"That's compliment enough, these days," said Menelaos. "What on earth possesses that woman!"

"Which one?"

"My wife."

"Well, that's about the same thing as I asked you when you came home," said Eteoneus, "and you were angry at me. Now, if you will tell me how to—"

"We've wandered from the subject," said Menelaos. "You've answered the first complaint against you. How about those sarcastic remarks?"

"I made them," said Eteoneus. "The woman refused to go away. She wanted to get at the scandal, from me if nobody else would talk to her. I said good day several times, in several fairly polite forms, but she stuck like a leach, and what with trying not to give information, and what with the annoyance of being questioned, I dare say I answered her a bit sharply."

"Do you remember anything you said?"

"I don't know that I do. I admit I felt snappish. . . . Oh, yes, she wanted to know whether Agamemnon didn't attack Clytemnestra and whether Clytemnestra didn't kill him in self-defense. I remember I said I'd submit the question to Helen as soon as she came in; she would know if her sister's husband tried to kill her and couldn't, or if the lady just killed her husband spontaneously. Something like that. I recall how annoyed Charitas looked."

"It does sound impertinent, and I'm sure it's softer than what you actually said."

"Menelaos, would you think better of my behavior if I gossiped with the neighbors about you and your relatives? What I think of Clytemnestra and what I think of your wife, is my private opinion—I believe you suggested as much; to talk of such things to Charitas is strictly none of my business. She wanted gossip; I couldn't get rid of her. Of course she'd be dissatisfied with my most diplomatic replies. I could have avoided her displeasure only by giving her the news. I hope you told her husband that his wife had little to do, inquiring into your affairs through your servants? I begin to think Helen was generous when she called her respectable!"

"Now, about the third complaint," said Menelaos, "I'd like to get on with this—there's something else we must talk of. Did you call her the meanest woman you'd met?"

"I dare say she is," said Eteoneus, "but I left her a loop-hole of escape. She said she would send her boy away, where he wouldn't be contaminated by the bad customs of this house, and I replied that if she separated him from Adraste now, she'd be the meanest woman I ever met, and I added that my experience was wide."

"But why does she speak of getting him away from my house?" said Menelaos. "He doesn't live here."

"Doesn't he! It's the only place he lives."

"You mean he's here?"

"Every minute he can be," said Eteoneus. "Helen told me not to let him come in, but you couldn't keep him out if there were a fifty-foot wall around the estate."

"This is the most complicated affair I've ever heard of!" said Menelaos. "My home appears to be in a condition of siege. Our one ambition, it seems, is to repell the Charitas family. Why did Helen wish to keep out the boy?"

"Adraste, of course."

"What are you talking about? . . . Oh, now I remember! . . . Helen was afraid the girl might fall in love with him."

"There was some danger of it," said Eteoneus.

"You think the danger is past?" said Menelaos.

"My, no!" said the gate-keeper; "it has happened—she's going to have a child by him."

"Merciful gods!" cried Menelaos; "in my house? a child? . . . I call that an outrage! . . . Is there a soul on the premises who isn't a disgrace to society? I call that downright immoral! Couldn't Helen stop it?"

"She wanted to—that was her purpose in trying to keep the boy out," said Eteoneus, "but you know how it is, Menelaos, when two youngsters are in love. You were young once yourself."

"Never!" said Menelaos, "never in that sense. I don't understand the point of view, though I know people who hold it. If that's right, I say, what is wrong?"

"Why, if they were married and the wife ran off with another man, I'd call that wrong," said Eteoneus. "And if the husband forgave her and took her back, or took her back without forgiving her, I'd call that wrong, or at least a grave error. But these young people are in love, and neither of them is of much importance out of love. I worried over Orestes and Hermione for fear they might do this very thing; in fact, I don't think much of Orestes for not justifying my fears. With a girl so important as Hermione, and you told me to take care of her, it would have been serious, but I'd like to know what's the harm if these two have done the natural thing? Helen doesn't like it because she thinks Damastor isn't good enough for the girl. Charitas is angry because she thinks the girl isn't good enough for Damastor. Between the two I rather side with Helen, but really they are both wrong."

"And the girl is going to have a child—in my house!"

"Yes, and Charitas is sending her boy away, so that he may not marry the girl, nor even see his own child occasionally," said Eteoneus. "I call that unnecessarily mean."

"I must see what can be done about it," said Menelaos.

"Nothing to do now but wait," said Eteoneus.

"Oh, yes, there is!" said Menelaos. "The child can be born somewhere else. My house can do very well without another scandal for a while, and I hate to think of the effect of such an episode upon my daughter. But to return to you, Eteoneus. There's another complaint against you, and your free ideas about Adraste fit in with it all too closely. You had a conversation with Hermione recently. I can't believe you said the things she reports, yet I trust her absolutely if she says so. About sex, of all subjects. You told her the lawless attitude men take toward women, and the sort of response women make to their advances, and to prove you knew what you were talking about, you told her of your own escapades in your youth. Hermione says it was the most suggestive talk she has heard, and she is profoundly shocked."

"I told her how we used to treat the women in war," said Eteoneus, "and I implied very delicately that the women rather liked it. Not a word that wasn't perfectly delicate, nor a syllable that wasn't true."

"But we don't tell that sort of truth to young girls now-a-days, Eteoneus. Hermione has led a sheltered life, and I want her to keep the innocence of youth as long as possible."

"Oh, come now, Menelaos, that's rather strong! Didn't I tell you when you came home that Hermione was full of new ideas, and didn't you pretend that you liked new ideas yourself? That was Hermione's last chance for the sheltered life, and it was probably too late then. Your notion of her mind is a generation behind time. I grew up in the rough days, which you can remember too, if you try. You think Hermione belongs to the next period, when the children were found in cabbages. She doesn't. Her generation are approaching the roughness again from the intellectual and moral point of view, and with a sense of duty. It's not healthy and I don't like it. A healthy person would know what sex is for; it's not a subject for meditation. Do you realize how I came to be discussing such matters with your sheltered daughter? She brought it on herself, speaking of Pyrrhus—she said he was a perfect brute with women, and she proved it by saying that he was living with Andromache. You see, she'd been interested to find that out. She was quite sure that men usually are bad at heart and seduce women. She evidently had given a lot of thought to the problem, and believed all the modern fictions. Wherever she got those ideas, she certainly did not get them from me. I might have told her much more than I did; far from being conscious

of any indiscretion, I now admire my restraint. I spoke
only about the brutality, as she called it, of men in war—
the Ajax-Cassandra sort of thing, which you yourself
thought not so bad. I never mentioned the way women
behave in times of peace. I never told her that if the
normally attractive man accepted all the invitations he
gets from respectable ladies, he'd have very little time to
himself. I merely said that the only people who could
testify as to the brutality of Pyrrhus were the women involved, and that probably, unless human nature is changing, they were devoted to him. That's about all I said—
along with testimony from my own experience."

"This is very strange," said Menelaos. "Helen was
telling her the same thing one day when I happened to
interrupt her. I wonder if my wife has been putting these
ideas into the child's head!"

"I don't think your wife would tell her that Pyrrhus
is a brute," said Eteoneus. "If she told her what I've just
said to you, she's almost the first woman I ever heard of
who could be honest on that subject. But Hermione and
I had talks about Orestes, as you remember, before you
came home, and she was beginning to have these ideas
then. It's too late in the world for the kind of innocence
you're wishing for, Menelaos. Everybody wants to know
everything—to talk about it, anyway. Besides, if Hermione didn't pick up the tendency for herself, she'd get
it from Orestes. I told you he was a bad influence."

"I detect a flaw in your logic," said Menelaos. "If it's
all right for you to talk frankly to a young girl, why isn't
it correct for Orestes to be just as frank on the same
themes? You ought to like Orestes—he's a man after
your own heart."

"I don't like him at all," said Eteoneus. "When I talk to Hermione or to any one else, I try to say what I've learned from experience. There's an element of life in it, I hope. That's what shocked Hermione. If I talk about women, because I've been pretty intimate with a lot of them, Hermione thinks me wicked, but if Orestes with no experience at all goes over the same ground, Hermione thinks him wise. Humbug! Mark my words, Menelaos, Orestes has a dirty mind, and he's a dangerous character. I admit he's strait-laced—it comes to the same thing. His kind want to talk about everything, but not to know about it. If a man is living like a saint, and has the thoughts of a saint, I'll say he's a saint. But if he's brooding on ideas which have no connection with his life, I don't trust his life, in the long run. The great thing is to be all of a piece. I'm suspicious of Orestes, and of Charitas, and I might as well say, of your daughter."

"If it weren't for certain differences in voice and features," said Menelaos, "I might think it was Helen talking to me. I never dreamed you shared her theories of life."

"I hope I don't," said Eteoneus. "Your wife isn't my ideal at all. I blame her for most of the trouble that's come on us."

"Whether you like her or not," said Menelaos, "you talk much the same way. That is, it sounds like part of her conversations. She's all for sincerity, you know, and her life has been mixed up in love-affairs. You're for sincerity too, it seems, and the revelation of your amorous past distressed my daughter. I begin to see what sincerity comes to."

"That's very well so far as I'm concerned," said

Eteoneus, "but you don't understand your wife. I'm sorry to say it, but she's too smart for you. The way she kept you from going off to help Orestes was one of the neatest things I've seen. Just an insinuation or two about Clytemnestra, and the awkwardness of arranging the marriage if you were implicated in the execution of her lover, and you actually gave up the impulse to have a share in avenging your brother! Then another hint or two about your brother's murderess at your daughter's wedding, and you decided against the wedding. That woman can get anything she wants. As long as you both live, she will turn you round her little finger. What I object to most is her knack of making people feel they're wrong and she's right. Most women have the gift, but with her it's an art. I dare say she made Priam think she came to Troy at considerable personal sacrifice, and the city owed her something. She says nothing to me—I suppose she can guess I don't like her; but when she turns on me that extraordinary look of hers, I feel sure she's ready to forgive me, any time I ask it."

"Forgive you what?" said Menelaos.

"Exactly! What?" said Eteoneus. "I've done nothing amiss, so far as I know. But that's your wife's attitude. The rest of us are always wrong, and there's no system in it. She is very indignant with Clytemnestra, who wasn't proper enough, and she objects to Charitas because she's too conventional!"

"Yes," said Menelaos, "and she doesn't like Orestes because of his family, but she has that girl Adraste with her all the time, and now Adraste has disgraced herself."

"I must admit I agree with Helen on the last two counts," said Eteoneus. "I don't care for Orestes myself, and Adraste's a very fine girl—one of the finest women you are likely to meet."

"I'm not likely to meet her," said Menelaos. "I've noticed her about the house, but I never pay much attention to the women servants. Now I'll send her away, and protect my home as completely as I can from this latest scandal. Where had I better send her, Eteoneus?"

"I'd leave it to Helen," said Eteoneus; "she'll know the best place."

"But Helen won't wish her to go," said Menelaos. "It would be just like her to keep the girl and make a heroine of her!"

"Very probably," said Eteoneus. "In my youth men had a firm way with women, especially with their wives; they just told them what to do or what not to, and disobedience meant a beating. If Hermione would give her consent, you might try that method on Helen. I wouldn't advise you to do anything about Adraste without your wife's permission, unless you really are prepared to revive that old-fashioned kind of argument."

"I'll see Helen about it, and I'll send the girl away," said Menelaos. "Thank you for your anxiety, Eteoneus, but I can still manage my own home. I don't need your advice as to disciplining my wife. You'll see, Adraste will go."

"I doubt if you need me in any way," said Eteoneus. "I'd like to retire as soon as you can find another gatekeeper."

"Do you mean that?" said Menelaos.

"I do."

"I can't let you go till this Orestes affair is well over," said Menelaos. "Don't be hasty in making up your mind.

I'll tell Charitas' husband you've made an apology which satisfies me, and I'll guarantee your courtesy in the future. I'll try to see that Hermione does not hold private conversations with you. When Orestes returns, let me know your final decision about the gate-keeping. I'd be glad to have you stay on. I should miss our occasional differences of opinion—we've had them for many years. You're almost the only person now with whom I can—well, never mind!"

II

MENELAOS looked worried. It may have been the accumulation of domestic disaster, or it may have been that he was about to demonstrate his ability to make Helen do what he wanted, but whatever the reason, he was haggard and suddenly old. He walked up and down several times, without any gain of confidence. Helen seemed prepared for something. She had an indefinable air of being amused. She never looked better.

"I'd like to talk with you about two matters," he said. "One of them I think will please you. Pyrrhus accepts your invitation."

"Your invitation," said Helen.

"Well, he accepts the invitation, and will shortly be here. He probably is on the way now. I hope you are satisfied!"

"What about?"

"You are having your own way, aren't you? A fine time to entertain him, with our household so—upset!"

"There couldn't possibly be a worse time," said Helen.

Menelaos walked up and down some more. He would pause in front of Helen, as though to give her his opinion, then he'd think better of it, and walk on. Helen looked a little sorry for him.

"Menelaos, you remember you invited Pyrrhus of your own accord—indeed, against my expressed desire. I suggested the visit, of course, and I even hoped Hermione and he might be interested in each other. When you discouraged that idea, I contented myself with the wish that Hermione at least might meet him, even though she chose Orestes. But when I saw how impossible it would be to receive him hospitably, I begged you to postpone the visit. You wouldn't listen to me, and now you are sorry he is coming. But I shall do my best to entertain him, and he probably won't stay long."

"On the contrary," said Menelaos, "if you do your best to entertain him, he probably will never leave. That's what I've been afraid of, all along. I think you had better keep in the background as much as possible and perhaps Hermione had better, also. I'll entertain him. The more I know of the men of the younger generation, the less I care to see my daughter with them. I'll entertain him, and I'll see that he goes home soon. The recent tragedy, in which your sister figured, will give you an excuse for secluding yourself."

Helen smiled at him, and he took to walking up and down again.

"Seclusion for me, certainly, but why for Hermione? She has been too much secluded already. The point of this visit, which seems to embarrass you, was merely to give her another idea of the world, to widen her acquaintance beyond this small place. I have entire confidence that even in my absence you can protect her from whatever danger there is in a few conversations with Pyrrhus."

"Quite true," said Menelaos, "but I foresee awkward possibilities. If Hermione should by chance fall in love with him now, Orestes might think I had Pyrrhus here for that purpose."

"You can always lay the blame on me, you know," said Helen.

"But Orestes is going to be angry anyway when I tell him he can't marry Hermione," said Menelaos, "and I want to keep the debate on a high plane—on the question of principle. My daughter can't marry the son of a woman who killed her husband. If Orestes hears that I'm trying to marry Hermione to Pyrrhus, he'll say my objection to the murder is just a device to break his engagement and win a more celebrated son-in-law."

"I don't see why you have to fear what Orestes thinks," said Helen. "After all, Hermione doesn't belong to him. He has done nothing to justify his pretensions to her hand, if indeed he wishes to marry her. Have you thought of that? Hermione wants him, but you and I have no reason to think he reciprocates. Treat Pyrrhus as you would if Orestes did not exist; it's the courteous way, and the only self-respecting."

"I wish I hadn't asked Pyrrhus!" said Menelaos. "Do you think it's too late now to postpone the visit?"

"Can the messenger reach him before he starts—or shortly after?" said Helen. "It wouldn't do to turn him back from your very door. If you could get word that your brother is dead, and that my sister killed him, Pyrrhus won't want to come, anyway, and he'll be glad to understand why we can't have him at present."

"I'll do that," said Menelaos. "I never wanted him, and it's not too late if the messenger hurries. . . . There's another thing, Helen. I hear that one of your girls in the house has been misbehaving."

"None of them, so far as I know," said Helen.

"Yes, what's her name—Adraste—is in trouble."

"If you call it misbehaving," said Helen. "Trouble is the more accurate word. A very respectable young man in the neighborhood has been making love to her."

"Damastor, isn't it? You told me something about the affair a while ago."

"Yes," said Helen, "it's Damastor."

"A very decent sort of boy, I've always thought. I didn't imagine he'd do anything improper."

"He wouldn't, in a direct way, but he has plenty of what you might call negative meanness. He made love to Adraste, as I say, and persuaded her that they were soul-mates, with vows of eternal faithfulness, and promises to marry her. A very old story. He meant it all—he's not a bad boy. But his mother has sent him out of harm's way, as she puts it, and he has allowed himself to be sent. In plain words, Adraste is deserted."

"You mean she has been living with him?"

"She will have a child very soon. I'm trying to cheer her up all I can. She's little more than a child herself; I wish she had been spared this early cruelty."

"I wish she had left that boy alone!" said Menelaos. "Didn't you know this scandal was going on?"

"This what?" said Helen.

"Scandal!" said Menelaos. "The word is familiar to you. A disreputable woman, employed in my house, misbehaving with the young son of my old friend and neighbor! It's no time for another scandal; my reputation can't stand it!"

He took to walking up and down again, and Helen looked past him, out toward the garden, as though he were not there.

"You ask me if I knew what was happening," she

began. "I knew they were in love, and as I said to you, you remember, I feared it would end badly. I advised Adraste not to lose her heart to Damastor if she could help it. She couldn't help it. The boy would not have run away if his mother had not compelled him. In my judgment Charitas is the scandalous person. If she had kept her hands off, there would have been an imprudent marriage. Thanks to her meddling, there is a clandestine love-affair and an illegitimate child."

"Good heavens, is the child here already?" said Menelaos.

"Not yet," said Helen.

"Then before it's too late we'll send the girl to some place where the child can be born without involving us. Afterward I'll provide for it's support so long as they stay away. Have you any place to suggest?"

"None," said Helen. "And it's not necessary. This is really the most convenient place I know."

"I don't think you understand me," said Menelaos.

"Perhaps I don't," said Helen. "I thought you asked me if I had any place to suggest where the child could be born without involving us. There is no such place. I am responsible for Adraste, and she depends upon me for comfort—even at that, she is in despair over Damastor's deserting her. In ordinary decency I am, in a way, involved. You are too, I should say."

"You never were more mistaken in your life," said Menelaos. "I have no responsibility in the matter, and I know what I am about when I say that the child should not be born in this house. It will do Hermione no good to become accustomed to such events in a supposedly well-ordered home. She is full of rather advanced ideas already, and her environment should be more normal rather than less so."

"If Hermione were to talk with Adraste now," said Helen, "she would see in the poor girl no encouragement to vice, no possible inducement toward indiscreet conduct. She might even learn from Adraste, in her present despondent mood, to avoid love altogether, and to distrust all men."

"You think first of Adraste," said Menelaos. "I am thinking of Hermione. Our daughter is entitled to a quiet and respectable home——"

"Then it's well you have abandoned your support of Orestes!" said Helen.

"——a thoroughly respectable home, and a certain amount of what is usually called innocence. It's wrong to force the ugly facts of life on a young girl's attention; they'll come soon enough of themselves. I'm sorry, but Adraste must go. It's very unfortunate."

"Very!" said Helen.

Menelaos stood looking at her a moment. "Well," he said, "I didn't like to speak of it, and I'm glad you don't oppose me."

Helen looked up at him, very steadily. "How could I oppose you," she said, "in any generous and proper intention? I assume that Adraste will stay."

"I have just told you with the utmost positiveness, that she will not stay!"

"I am sure you will change your mind," said Helen, "I have complete confidence in you."

"No," said Menelaos, "on other occasions I have given in to you, but this time I can't. I've made the decision."

"Have you?" said Helen.

"I say I have!" said her husband.

"Then you have, and no doubt of it," said his wife.

"I'm glad you see it my way," said Menelaos. "I thought you would."

"Menelaos, you thought nothing of the kind!" said Helen. "You knew I should never agree to sending the girl away. I never shall. Adraste remains in this house as long as I do."

Menelaos hated to believe his eyes; she was laughing at him.

"If you make me angry," he said, "I'll have that girl carried out and thrown into the street!"

"I don't wish to make you angry," she said, "but I doubt if you can get any one to execute your amiable commands. The household are all fairly kind-hearted, and Adraste is exceedingly popular with them."

"Take your choice," said Menelaos. "Either you will aid me in sending that girl to a place we agree on, or I'll have her put out of this house!"

"I dare you to!" said Helen. "Now, that's a fair challenge! Your men wouldn't lay a finger on that girl. I defy you to give the order. They will think you have gone crazy, and I will tell them, quite sincerely, that I think so too. It will make a stir, won't it, though! And you wished to avoid further notoriety! Wouldn't it be rare justice if Pyrrhus came along just as the heroic Menelaos was throwing out into the street a sick and helpless girl, about to become a mother! You could explain it to him afterward, couldn't you! You could say it was a belated but needed house-cleaning. The servants, you could say, were beginning to behave as badly as the gentle folk, and since you couldn't reform your relatives, you had decided to discharge the domestics. I wish Achilles could hear that!"

"Very witty, I'm sure," said Menelaos, "but you can't talk me out of it. Adraste can leave quietly, or if she insists on staying where she isn't wanted, I'll have her put out!"

He waited for Helen to speak, but she said nothing. She looked calm and much at her ease.

"You can't prevent me, you know, if I've made up my mind."

"If I wished to prevent you," she said, "I'd simply ask the men not to do it. I'd explain your temporary insanity. I'd remind them that even when you are yourself you have little respect for the proprieties—as when you cut short those sacrifices at Troy. The men still talk about that sojourn on the island and in Egypt. But I should not try to prevent this madness, if you were determined upon it; you are your own master, and I should let you go to your fate."

"Now see here, Helen," said Menelaos, "what will you do with Adraste if she stays? She won't be of any possible use to you, with a baby to look after, and there's no future for her when the child grows up."

"She'll be a companion always—she's one of the best, and I like children," said Helen. "She'll be a daughter in the house when Hermione marries and leaves us."

"Hermione isn't going to marry very soon," said Menelaos. "She won't have Pyrrhus, and I won't have Orestes."

"But Hermione will, I think," said Helen. "She's going to marry Orestes. Didn't you know that?"

"I didn't and I don't," said Menelaos.

"Well, she is," said Helen, "and you might as well make up your mind to it. I don't want it any more than you do, but we can't stop it. I found that out talking to her. That's why I gave up hope of Pyrrhus. You opposed me, but you would have come around in time. Hermione's state of mind made it impossible."

"She shan't marry Orestes! I've forbidden it!"

"You've done all you could," said Helen, "and she will now do what she likes. Don't worry about having to negotiate with Clytemnestra; I'm sure Hermione will tell us some day they're already married—or she'll tell me I'm to be a grandmother. I shan't ask you to throw her out of the house."

"Helen, I'd like to meet you half-way," said Menelaos. "You were right about Orestes, when I still believed in him. I'll join you in preventing his marriage to Hermione if you'll arrange with me to get Adraste off somewhere to avoid talk. People like your neighbor Charitas—"

"In this case Charitas won't talk," said Helen. "You forget she is hiding the missing husband. As for Hermione, I meant what I said—we are powerless. But whether we are or not, I stand by Adraste. It's a point of honor. I love the girl, and she is in trouble. After all, Menelaos, don't you think it's too late? You are a kind man, and naturally easy-going, and you've put up with too much to discover a shocking scandal in this wretched little tragedy. You took me back, and you've done nothing to avenge your brother's death. I'm not complaining, of course, but after those exhibitions of magnanimity you are not convincing when you improvise righteous indignation over Adraste and her child. Now, if you don't think it's too late, you may change your character, become quite firm, and rule us with a rod. Put Adraste out, lock me up when Pyrrhus comes, see to it that Hermione doesn't marry Orestes. There were to be other penalties, weren't there, if we didn't obey you? Impose them all now, Menelaos, for if you are cruel to Adraste I shall become your implacable enemy. My family has a gift for hate—though until now I never cultivated it."

"I dare say you could emulate Clytemnestra if you wished," said Menelaos.

"My dear husband, if I wished, I could surpass her! Clytemnestra was crude and unnecessarily vulgar. But I shan't become your enemy unless you force the issue— and only for a principle, never for a lover. I want to keep the debate on a high plane."

"I hope I may be able to discern the difference when you stick the knife into me," said Menelaos. "Meanwhile, I'll take my chance. Adraste is to go; that's understood. You and I are to be mortal enemies; that's understood also. Do you mind telling me just how the war between us is to begin?"

"There are several possible ways," said Helen. "You might kill me—consider Troy merely postponed. That would be rather neat; Agamemnon's brother getting even with Clytemnestra's sister! Or you might carry out your threat and tell your men to put Adraste on the street. If they disobey, you might carry her out yourself. I advise the first course."

"And I dare say, in your present resigned mood, you'll wait for the fatal blow to fall."

"Yes," said Helen, "unless Pyrrhus arrives first."

"Ah, that's it, is it? What will he do for you?"

"I suppose that depends on what I ask him to do, and that, of course, depends on what you decide to do. . . . Oh, Menelaos, what's the use of this half-hearted quarreling? You won't do anything unkind to Adraste, I know perfectly well, and I understand the embarrassment her plight causes you. I'm sorry! If I let such things bother me, I should be embarrassed too, for people will say my bad example led her to do wrong. As things have turned out, I'm sorry I asked you to have Pyrrhus; you invited him because I wanted it, and now I own it was a mistake on my part. But wouldn't you say all this is a small matter, in comparison with what you and I have on our hearts? When I think of my sister, of our girlhood, of what she has done, Adraste's predicament seems far from the worst of tragedies. Meanness and treachery are the tragic thing, aren't they? And seeing life out of proportion. Let's be friends, dear husband! Why should it be unpleasant to remember that once we were lovers?"

III

"Is MOTHER here?" said Hermione. "Oh, there you are! Father the most terrible thing has happened, and I want to tell you of it in mother's presence. Adraste, that girl, is going to have a child!"

"I know it," said Menelaos.

"You know it? And you can let such a thing happen in your house, and be so calm about it? I was blaming mother in my thoughts as I hurried home—but you knew about it all the time!"

"Hermione, you shouldn't speak so to your father," said Helen. "This is not the first occasion I have had to object to your manner."

"There are worse things in this house than my manner," said Hermione, "and even if you and father don't feel outraged by them, I do. If that girl is to remain with us, after this disclosure, I decline to live here."

"Where will you go?" asked Helen.

"I don't know—perhaps to Orestes, as my duty seems to call me. I may be of use to him—I can be of no use here. I've tried to be loyal and respectful to both my parents, but we are comparative strangers, and our relation is essentially false. Your affairs are more and more tangled and, I should say, hopeless, but they seem to be what you want. The honest thing for me to do is to marry Orestes at once, and begin over again, in the simple and usual way of sane people."

"That kind of talk is very distasteful, daughter," said Menelaos. "I don't refer to your manner toward me; the distressing thing is your lack of sympathy for people in difficulties. Your mother and I have had great sorrows recently, for which we were not responsible—scandalous sorrows. Fortunately, we can bear them without your help, but if you were as normal as you say you wish to be, you would be sorry for us, not take us to task. Adraste is the latest. I'm not responsible for her, as you would have known had you waited a minute—"

"Then prove it," said Hermione. "Put her out of the house!"

"You mean, just put her out, to starve or die of suffering?" said Helen.

"Yes, that's what I mean!" said Hermione.

"At times, as I've always remarked, you resemble your aunt," said Helen, "but I never saw the likeness so strong."

"The resemblance doesn't interest me, and I can't admire your attempt to divert the conversation," said Hermione. "This revelation of the conditions in our house has put me beyond patience. It was bad enough when you went to Troy with Paris, and bad enough when you returned and insisted that you had been there, and had done all the wrong attributed to you; even at that, the scene of your exploits was far away, and people didn't need to believe the worst unless they wanted to. But that girl has been misbehaving right here, where you can't keep a secret from the neighbors. Ever since she came she has been flirting with Damastor, a nice boy, thoroughly unspoiled, until she led him astray. I don't see why we should lend our good name—I won't lend mine—to shelter her and her vulgar instincts!"

"Have you talked with her since you heard the news?" said Helen.

"I wouldn't be seen talking with her!"

"Then do it surreptitiously. You could profit by it—any of us could. You can't imagine yourself in her place, can you? Abandoned by a man you trusted—Orestes, for instance—and become a theme of household gossip?"

"I certainly can't imagine myself," said Hermione. "You can't imagine me either!"

"I shan't try to," said Helen. "The point I would make is that until the thing happened to her, Adraste, like you, could not imagine herself caught in such misery. That's life, daughter. Most of us are hard on others because we are unimaginative."

"Did you warn her of this possibility when you were telling her to cultivate the love of life?" said Hermione.

Menelaos laughed.

"I warned her against the love of Damastor," said Helen, "just as I tried to teach you the love of life, and advised you not to love Orestes. You both, in different ways, thought you knew better than I."

"There's some difference between Orestes and Damastor," said Hermione.

"But not nearly enough," said her father. "I agree that Adraste ought to go into some sort of retirement, away from the publicity she enjoys here; I was talking it over with your mother when you came in. I was telling her also that Pyrrhus has accepted our invitation, and will soon arrive. We are thinking of postponing the visit. But if he does come, I want you to entertain him with the best courtesy of the house. You won't need to see too much of him, but he must go home thinking well of us. That is, if he comes."

"I'm glad there's a chance of his not coming," said Hermione. "I don't care to see him. Eteoneus understands him, and Adraste, and mother, but I have nothing in common with his type. In fact, I won't see him, even if he does come!"

"You will if I tell you to!" said Menelaos.

"Father, don't tell me to," said Hermione. "I'd hate to disobey you, but nothing could induce me to talk to that man. Every word I said would seem disloyal."

"Disloyal to whom?" said Helen.

"To Orestes. Father ought to tell Pyrrhus I'm engaged to Orestes. Pyrrhus, I feel, is looking for a wife, and in every moral obligation I'm practically a married woman."

"We might as well straighten this out, once for all," said Menelaos. "You're not married to Orestes, are you?"

"Not yet," said Hermione.

"And I won't insult you by asking whether you have ignored the legal ceremony, in Adraste's fashion. Very well. Please understand that unless circumstances greatly change, we don't consider Orestes an eligible husband for you. We have abandoned all idea of that match. You are pledged to nobody. And if you meet Orestes secretly, without my permission, I'll call him to severe account, and you too!"

"Menelaos," said Helen, "don't you think we are going about this in the wrong way? You and I don't wish Hermione to marry Orestes, but it's no use forbidding her to do so. She's not a child. In fact, she may soon develop the traits of a spinster. And if you make threats, you'll have to keep them."

"Of course I'll keep them!" said Menelaos. "Up to date I've been too mild, but I've learned my lesson. You always do what you like. Now if Hermione begins to imitate you in that respect, I see the last vestige of a good home disappearing."

"I'm not imitating mother—it's unfair even to imply such a thing," said Hermione. "I merely keep my word with the man I'm formally engaged to. I'm trying to stand somewhat for the proprieties."

"Humbug!" said Helen. "You don't mean what you say, or you don't know what you're saying. If you are resolved to marry Orestes in order to illustrate a propriety, stop now. The man will not want propriety—he will ask for love."

"I hardly need to say that I love him, but I do need to remind you, mother, that with Orestes and me love is not necessarily a contrast to propriety. Let me say I'm trying to stand for what I've always admired. I haven't changed, and I can't say you have, but father has. A few weeks ago he agreed with all my sentiments; now he agrees with yours. Quite within his rights, to agree with you if he can. But I ought not to be persecuted just because I refuse to change."

"Yes, in the last few weeks I've adopted another attitude toward Orestes," said Menelaos, "and if you can't see why, I'm sorry for you. You think your mother's influence caused the defection. Your sense of what is proper permits you to overlook the fact in the last few weeks Orestes' mother has murdered my brother. That would strain even the friendliest relations. You have very little delicacy of sentiment, Hermione, or you wouldn't be so ambitious to marry into that family."

"I've delicacy enough to be sorry for the murder, but—"

"Well, I'm thankful you go even so far," said Menelaos.

"If you're sarcastic, I shan't continue!" said Hermione.

"Don't continue," said Helen. "Enough has been said. But I'd like to ask you a question—coming back to Adraste. When you entered just now you told us you had hurried in as soon as you heard the news. Who gave you the news?"

"Charitas," said Hermione. "She wasn't gossiping; it came about in the most natural way. I stopped in there for a minute, and she had to explain Damastor's absence. She feels very bitter about the whole thing. It seems you took Adraste there one day, and she saw the boy."

"Helen," said Menelaos, "you assured me that Charitas wouldn't talk!"

"I underrated her sense of the proprieties," said Helen. "So she's the one who gave you that character-portrait of Adraste! Did she imply in any way that Damastor may have collaborated in wrong-doing?"

"Certainly not!" said Hermione. "You can't blame a mere boy, in the hands of such a person. That kind of woman can do what she likes with a man, anyway."

"Oh, I don't know!" said Menelaos. "It depends on the man."

"And on the woman," said Helen. "Continue, Hermione—what else did she say?"

"She says you brought it all about. When you first came home, she says, you called on her—"

"I called on her!"

"—and you gave a frank statement of your ethical theories in such matters. If she had understood how entirely you meant it, she says, she might have been on her guard. You told her that Damastor ought to fall in love with the first pretty girl he met, and you had Adraste along at the time, to ensnare him."

"As much as to say that Adraste was the first beauty he met. Not counting you, of course. On that same occasion Charitas told me Damastor was interested in you."

"She couldn't have told you that—he never was."

"Well, what else did she say now?"

"That's the substance, I think—she elaborated it."

"She probably has forgotten one or two things I told her," said Helen. "I pointed out that her desire to keep Damastor respectable would probably make him immoral. She didn't mention that? Very odd! . . . What purpose does she think I could have in seducing her son through Adraste?"

"I'd rather not answer that question," said Hermione.

"Answer it just the same," said her father. "That interests me."

"Well, she gave practically the same explanation as you did, father, when we were talking a while ago; she said it was mother's age. Women of a certain type, she said, try to exercise their charms vicariously as they grow older."

"That sounds like Charitas, but not like your father."

"He said just that—didn't you say it?"

"He never said it, and he doesn't think it," answered Helen. "In fact, if Pyrrhus comes, he desires me to keep to my room. In your father's eyes I may some day be vicarious, but not yet."

"That was my idea," said Hermione. "I told him that."

"Of course I'm flattered to have you women arguing about what I say and think," said Menelaos, "but at the moment I'm more interested in what Charitas says. I'm getting a picture of my household from the outside."

"She didn't speak of the household," said Hermione; "only about mother, and of course about Damastor and that girl."

"We know what she said about the girl. What provision will she make for her grandchild?" said Helen.

"For her what?"

"There's going to be a child, and Charitas is its grandmother. Haven't you visualized the whole situation? Charitas has—that's where the sting lies. Her mind runs on age because she's a grandmother first."

"Oh, no, you're wrong, she doesn't think of it as her grandchild; she spoke of it as though—well, as though it were a disease. I doubt if she will provide for it."

"I thought she wouldn't," said Helen. "Your father and I shall have to, and perhaps it's as safe for the child."

"I'll do nothing of the kind!" said Menelaos. "I told you Adraste must leave the house— Hermione, I was telling your mother that when you came in."

"Yes, he was. You see, my daughter, how improper it was of you to address your father as you did. He was agreeing with you entirely. We haven't had as much murder as we'd like; you and Charitas and Menelaos, the three props of society in our neighborhood, all wish to kill Adraste and her baby. I am holding out against you for their right to live. But I'm not committed to keeping the girl here, if another arrangement would be better for her. I can think of one such arrangement. She ought to be with Damastor. If Charitas will tell us where she has sent Damastor, I'll send Adraste there at once."

"She'll never tell you!"

"Probably not, but I can't see why she won't, daughter. I'm no judge, you will say, but the kind of respectability that recommends itself to me, would send the girl to her lover, and permit them to marry. You approve of marriage? That's what these young people want."

"I never thought of that," said Menelaos, "but it's an excellent suggestion. If we could get them married—and away from here—I'd say we were well out of a bad business. I wonder if it could be arranged?"

"Very simply," said Helen. "Hermione has the confidence of Charitas, it seems. I'll keep out of the negotiations. Let Hermione go to Charitas, as from you, with the promise that if she will tell us where the boy is, we will send Adraste there, at our own costs, see that they are honorably married, and give them enough to start life on together, in some distant place where no gossip will attach to them."

"That's the thing!" said Menelaos. "I'll do that."

"But can't you understand Charitas' point of view?" said Hermione. "She wants to separate them forever. Adraste will never make Damastor happy—a woman of that kind; if Charitas had wished to see him married to her, she wouldn't have sent him away. Your plan would be admirable for Adraste, but it would do nothing for Charitas."

"Wouldn't it do something for Damastor?" said

Helen. "He loves the girl, and I presume Charitas loves him somewhat—it can't be all a question of wounded pride."

"Charitas will never tell where Damastor is," said Hermione.

"I'm half afraid you are right," said Helen, "but I want you to carry the message from your father, just the same. We shall have done what we could for the young people, and we shall have assumed responsibility for what happened in our home, though I personally do not condemn Adraste and Damastor as you do. If Charitas won't meet us half-way, the responsibility will then be hers, and you will have an opportunity to learn something of human nature."

"I'm sorry," said Hermione. "I know without asking that Charitas won't do what you want—and really, I don't care to ask her."

"Why not, pray?" said Menelaos.

"I think she is right in sending Damastor out of that girl's influence. It would not be for his happiness to marry her."

"Doesn't he love her any more? And oughtn't people to marry if they love each other?" said Helen. "You ought to be giving me the arguments I'm urging. I'm such a liberal that I begin to seem conservative. If people do wrong, they ought to mend and do right—you still think so, don't you? You think people ought not to live together if they're not married. I hope you think people ought to marry if they love each other, and not otherwise. Well, let us give Damastor and Adraste the chance to conform to society, even though it's a bit late. They wish to conform."

"I don't know that they do," said Hermione. "Charitas has no confidence in Adraste, and neither have I."

"You don't know Adraste very well. But look at it from Damastor's point of view. When you were talking about Pyrrhus and what you called his brutalities, I thought you condemned the men who abandoned women. Damastor didn't abandon Adraste, but his mother has produced the same effect by abducting him. Wouldn't it be well if Charitas now gave him the opportunity to act as I suppose he'd like to—as a loyal man?"

"I don't take your point of view," said Hermione.

"I'm shocked at you, Hermione," said Menelaos; "I'm really shocked. You told me that you and Orestes are practically married, that nothing must be allowed to separate you. Adraste and Damastor are more married than you are, yet you think they should be kept apart at any inconvenience to them or to others."

"There's no parallel between these people and Orestes and me," said Hermione. "We have done our best to lead good lives, whereas Adraste and Damastor have been purely selfish—if I must say it right out, they have been sensual and beastly. I have felt for a long time that our home was deteriorating, but I never thought it would come to this, that you and mother would countenance impropriety of a gross kind, and would even ask me to aid the culprits. Mother repeats her sneers at the respectable, but worse than anything she says is the lax attitude you both take toward ordinary morals. Damastor should never have had anything to do with that girl, but since he made one mistake, I admire his mother's resolution to prevent him from repeating it. My contempt for Adraste I can not express. I will do nothing to cover over her faults and restore her to a place in society which she does not deserve. And if she is to remain here, I repeat what I said when I came in—I will not stay in the same house with her!"

"You give up your parents as hopeless, do you?" said Menelaos. "You pretend to judge me, burdened as I am with this and many other problems, yet you will not do what I ask to relieve one of them? Who is selfish now, I'd like to know?"

"You are," said Hermione. "You and mother have piled up one difficulty after another for yourselves, and you wish me to help you out even at the loss of my self-respect and the sacrifice of my principles. It would do no good for me to speak to Charitas, and I should have lost the reputation I enjoy—the only member of the family—for acceptable behavior. Don't think I'm without affection for you, or that I relish the idea of leaving my home for such a reason as this. But I have a right to be myself. People who talk most about leading their own lives—people like mother—usually have to involve others before they get through."

"You break my heart," said Menelaos; "I've done nothing, and asked you to do nothing, which would justify such talk as this. If you wish to leave this house, do so. I'll have a talk with Orestes as soon as I can. He ought to know about this from our point of view. You'll give him your own version."

"Hermione," said Helen, "you didn't want to marry Damastor, did you?"

"I certainly did not!"

"I never could understand why women are so jealous of men they don't themselves want to marry," said Helen. "Nor why murder is easier to forgive than beauty."

IV

"May I come in?" said Eteoneus. "I don't wish to interrupt, but I notice that the whole family are here, and I prefer to tell the news to you all at once."

"News about what?" said Menelaos.

"About Orestes."

They looked at him and were silent. He waited for a question to help him out, but at last he had to go on by himself.

"It's partly good news, and partly bad. In the first place, the young man has avenged his father's death. He has killed Ægisthus."

"That's something like!" said Menelaos. "I thought Orestes could manage it alone, and there's a special satisfaction when the son can take care of his father's memory; it shows the line hasn't run out. That's very good news, Eteoneus."

"You usually give us the outline first and the details afterward," said Helen. "May we hear the details?"

"The messenger says that Ægisthus has been growing nervous over a possible attempt at revenge; he couldn't learn where Orestes was, and he lived under the unpleasant possibility of a knife in his ribs at any moment. Clytemnestra stood the strain very well, or perhaps she didn't feel it, but at last Ægisthus rather went to pieces. He took to religion. Every morning he would steal out to the domestic altar—you remember the place, Menelaos, where your brother smoothed off a few rocks for the family devotions; and there Ægisthus would sacrifice a small animal, and ask for protection till the next dawn. Clytemnestra never joined him, the messenger says—she put no trust in sacrifices. So the unhappy king used to slip out there alone, before his morning's duties began. Orestes waited around the place in hiding till he had learned this habit of his enemy's. Then one morning when Ægisthus was watching the flame intently, Orestes stole up and cut his head off. That's all there was to it."

"I knew he would show his ability," said Menelaos. "This puts him rather high in my esteem. If it weren't for his mother—"

"Can't you overlook his mother," said Hermione, "now that he has behaved so well? You said that this test would show his character. Now be just, father, and admit I have chosen a good husband."

"If this qualifies for the duties of a husband, why, he qualifies," said Helen. "But he won't be avenging murders all his life, and I hope you will marry him, if you do, for other reasons than his adroitness in killing Ægisthus. Where is he, Eteoneus? I'd like to meet Orestes."

"He's on the way, I understand," said Eteoneus, "but I doubt if he calls unless you give him a special invitation. He thinks the family doesn't approve of him, with the exception of your daughter, and just now he's—well, rather tense and sensitive."

"Could you get a special invitation to him? Then do so, by all means. You want him to come, don't you, Menelaos?"

"I'd like very much to see him," said Menelaos. "Is

he going to return that armor you lent him, Eteoneus?
It was my best set."

"Oh, he'll bring it back, Menelaos; I fancy he's reliable in such matters. He'll be wanting to get away
from that place as soon as he can, and this would be the
natural spot for him to hurry to."

"He won't care to stay near his mother very long,"
said Helen. "This is the worst that has happened to Clytemnestra—to have her lover executed right on the estate, where she thought herself so powerful!"

"Will you give your consent now to the marriage?"
said Hermione.

"No," said Menelaos. "You have the logic of the
situation, I admit, but I still don't feel he's the man for
you. While Eteoneus has been telling us the news, I've
been trying to explain why my heart is so depressed; I'm
glad of the vengeance, but I suppose it's the thought that
now you'll want to marry Orestes—nothing else could
make me morbid. I feel as though I had lost my best
friend, and Ægisthus wasn't that."

"Eteoneus," said Helen, "what did Clytemnestra
say?"

"Nothing."

"And what did she do?"

"Nothing."

Helen looked at him so steadily that they all looked
at her, and noticed that the color had left her face.

"You have bad news, too," she said. "Tell us everything."

"I see you've guessed it," said Eteoneus, "and that
makes it easier to tell. Clytemnestra's dead."

Helen rose to her feet, as if she were about to leave

them. Then she stood perfectly still, while the others talked.

"That's why Orestes handled it so smoothly," said Menelaos. "If she had been alive then, I dare say she would have been on the watch."

"No wonder Ægisthus took to sacrificing, with her gone. They really loved each other, I think," said Hermione. "How did she die, Eteoneus?"

"Orestes killed her."

"No!" cried Hermione.

"He killed her."

"Not his own mother!"

"His own mother."

"Orestes!"

"Helen," said Menelaos, "this is a good deal worse than my brother's death. There is no forgiveness in Heaven or on earth for such a crime. Orestes is a lost soul. Clytemnestra, in comparison, was a good woman. I hope I may never see—"

"I think Hermione is fainting," said Helen.

"I'm all right," said Hermione. "I don't blame your father—it's impossible—even if I had seen him do it, I'd say it's impossible. Orestes loved her, and he had the deepest sense of filial duty—it's simply impossible!"

"If you mean he didn't do it, you're wrong," said Eteoneus. "He killed her. It was one filial duty against another, and he took vengeance all around. He knows you won't like it—nobody seems to approve That's why he's sensitive about coming here."

"He can never come here," said Menelaos. "My wife knew how difficult it would be to meet the murderess of my brother; certainly she will never be asked to receive in our own house the son who killed her sister. That marriage is settled once for all. I take it your special invitation is withdrawn, Helen."

"For the time only," said Helen. "I'm sorry for Orestes. Whatever emotions I have besides, I'm chiefly sorry for a serious and stupid boy who could do such a thing by way of being dutiful. He is a lost soul, Menelaos, but I don't want him to be more lost than necessary. Imagine how he will feel when he realizes what he has done! Perhaps we ought to send for him now, rather than later. Yes, send for him, Menelaos!"

"I can't follow that," said Menelaos.

"Nor I," said Eteoneus. "These new ideas go too far. Killing Ægisthus was only proper, of course, but when it comes to killing your mother—I'll not open the gate to a man who has killed his own mother."

"I don't want him to come," said Hermione. "It would be too terrible with the whole household around. I think I had better see him first alone."

"You'll see him nowhere," said her father. "For this family Orestes does not exist. . . . If it were not too late! . . . When this horror has died out a little, we'll send for Pyrrhus again, and if he's what your mother thinks, you may marry him. He may have a fault or two, but we can no longer be fastidious. I'd rather like an alliance with Pyrrhus, to give us a standing again before the world."

"I was going to tell you, as another piece of news," said Eteoneus, "that Pyrrhus will probably be here in a day or two. He started more quickly than we expected, and I told the man we sent, according to your instructions, not to turn him back if he had got more than half-way."

"I think I'll retire, if you don't mind," said Hermione. "My head begins to ache terribly, and I must be alone for a while."

"Before you go," said Eteoneus, "there's something else I ought to tell you about Orestes. I don't greatly admire the young man, but it is only fair to say that perhaps he didn't do the actual killing—perhaps. There's a story that he preferred not to kill his mother, but merely stood by and watched it done."

"Oh, I hope that's true!"

"I can't see the distinction," said Menelaos. "To all intents he did it himself."

"Yes," said the gate-keeper, "there isn't much difference, but I thought what little there is might comfort Hermione."

"If he didn't kill her," said Helen, "who did?"

"His sister, Electra."

"You don't mean he let his sister do it for him?" said Menelaos.

"It's only a rumor—the messenger says no one knows just how it was done. You see, Electra hasn't been living with her mother and Ægisthus, whether she wouldn't, or they wouldn't have her, you can guess for yourself. As soon as Orestes had killed Ægisthus, he hurried to the little house where Electra was staying—I believe she was married or something; I remember she was in a peculiar situation, anyway—and Electra had asked her mother to call on her early that morning. Clytemnestra came, not suspecting the hospitable invitation, and Electra welcomed her cordially, then got her to enter the house, where Orestes was concealed, and there they killed her. Which one actually did it, you'll have to ask Orestes."

"Don't tell us any more!" said Menelaos. "The further you get, the worse it is. They betrayed her through hospitality. They asked her to come to her daughter's home, to kill her! You can't think of a sin they haven't committed! To reverence your parents comes first, with any people who are above the beasts; next after that comes the duty to the guest."

"That's how Orestes felt long ago, the time I wouldn't let him in," said Eteoneus. "He thought we were completely demoralized because we weren't hospitable. But I suppose he and his sister excused themselves by remembering the way Clytemnestra welcomed Agamemnon home from Troy; she went through the motions of hospitality, too. On the other hand, you could say that he was a husband, and the laws of hospitality didn't apply."

"Eteoneus," said Helen, "what sound reason have you for thinking that Electra did the killing?"

"Why, that idea sprang up from things Electra said afterward. When the vengeance was complete, they had the bodies of Ægisthus and Clytemnestra brought out, and called the people together to tell them what had happened—they were paralleling Clytemnestra in that, you see. But when the crowd gathered, Orestes and Electra couldn't get their mind off their dead mother lying there; they both collasped, you might say, pretty badly, Electra worse than her brother, and they accused themselves publicly. The messenger says it was awful to listen to. Electra kept saying she did it, and though Orestes claimed a share in the guilt, he didn't contradict her. But you can't judge by things said at such a moment."

"Father," said Hermione, "I believe it was Electra. She urged him on. I knew it wasn't like Orestes to do it. He will share the blame out of loyalty, but she did it, I'm sure. It's not nearly so bad as it seemed."

"It's so bad that I'll never let Orestes cross my threshold," said Menelaos. "You keep on looking for excuses, but the fact is, he killed his mother. If you have any of those natural feelings which are supposed to indicate the difference between right and wrong, you know he did wrong—so great a wrong that from now on he has lost his place in human society. You aren't thinking of him still as a husband, are you?"

"Certainly. He is my husband."

"Hermione, don't tell me you would marry a man who had killed his mother!"

"I shall marry him."

"Would a child of mine have a soul so mean? Don't say that, Hermione—think what you're saying! His wife will be as he is, the companion of his sin, utterly cursed. You will never enter a good home, nor sit down to eat with friends, nor even die in peace, nor rest in a quiet grave. If you think you love him, remember you must have no children—the curse must die with you! I can imagine how profoundly you are shocked by this horrible deed, but you don't yet realize the horror. Think it over quietly for a few days; you'll see that I'm right."

"You have told me the truth about my future," said Hermione, "but it still is my future. I belong to Orestes, to his curse, to his misery. I could never respect myself if I deserted him now. You don't know him as I do, and perhaps you never could understand his type of character. You are adventurous in battle, so I'm told, and

mother is adventurous in love. There are people who
are adventurous in duty—who will carry a thing through
not because it is pleasant, nor because they like it, nor
because it will make anybody happy, but because it is
right."

"You call it being adventurous in duty to kill your
mother?"

"In some circumstances, perhaps, but I was thinking
of myself, and of my duty to Orestes. I shall go through
with it."

"Whether or not it makes anybody happy, eh?"

"Menelaos," said Helen, "you were wise to say that
Hermione needs time to realize what all this means.
Give her time. You don't need to tell her to think it
over. She will be able to think of nothing else. In a few
days we can all talk more sanely. Nothing matters very
much after what has occurred. Nothing new could seem
very bad, not even her marriage to Orestes. But Orestes
himself must make fresh plans for his life, and we can
wait till we see him or hear from him."

"Till we hear from him," said Menelaos. "He can't
come to this house."

"He probably won't come now, anyway," said Eteoneus. "I remember they say he is going on a religious
journey, a pilgrimage to a shrine somewhere, to see if he
can rest his mind. The change will probably do him
good, anyway, and he won't be back for some time. One
way and another, your relatives do a lot of traveling,
Menelaos."

"That's in the past now," said Menelaos. "It's time
to settle down, and my immediate family are home to
stay, I believe. Hermione may think this over as long as

she likes, Helen, but I shall now proceed on an entirely
new plan. I'm going to find out if Pyrrhus will marry
her. You were right in the first place. If he will have
her, we'll let Orestes go on his pilgrimage, and it will be
a long one. If I criticized Pyrrhus, at least it was for
faults I could understand. He's overrated, but he's a
real man, and he can give Hermione the kind of home
she ought to have. It is providential that he got started
quickly on this visit."

"Oh, Menelaos, you're quite wrong to force the question again!" said Helen. "Let the whole problem rest a
while. Hermione doesn't need to marry, if she prefers
to stay with us, and certainly she must not marry a man
she doesn't love."

"Now see here, Helen, you make me very angry! You
stirred up this whole quarrel about Pyrrhus—if it hadn't
been for you we never should have thought of him
again. You've been persuading me with all sorts of in-
sidious arguments, and these recent events have com-
pleted my conversion. Why do you get on the other side
now? Hermione may think it over. When Pyrrhus
comes, I'll speak to him. Perhaps he won't have anything to do with us, but if he'll consider the proposal,
we'll go on from there."

"I'm sorry my future has given you so much trouble,"
said Hermione, "and I wish you wouldn't put yourself to
this unnecessary bother with Pyrrhus. But I'm not in a
position to say anything, and you know best what you
want to do. If I have your permission, I'll go now."

"Now, I wonder why Helen went with her," said
Menelaos. "I'd like to hear what they're saying to each

other, in private. Why do you think my wife has changed her mind about Pyrrhus?"

"She hasn't, I should say, but she sees it's useless," said Eteoneus. "Your daughter's going to marry Orestes. I don't know how, nor when, but Orestes is as good as a married man from now on."

"But he hasn't a thing in the world! He can't support a wife with this curse on him. It's the last moment you'd think he would choose for matrimony."

"I didn't say he'd choose—I said she would marry him. A sense of duty once roused is an awful thing, Menelaos. Women have such a turn for making it fit in with what they want to do anyway. She'll marry him, and later on he'll hear, from time to time, of the sacrifices she made for his benefit. Poor devil!"

"But she went out quite docile," said Menelaos. "She practically gave in to me, didn't you notice? And I count on Helen to follow up the advantage when they're alone. She wants Pyrrhus more than I do, and she must abhor the thought of Orestes now."

"That's so, but your wife is pretty shrewd, I must say, in the way she retires from an argument. She seems to know when she has won it, and also when she has lost it. That's rare in a woman. It's Helen's gift for accepting a fact that makes her so hard to manage. Helen didn't like your bringing up the marriage question just now—I could see that. I fancy she thinks you finally threw your case away. Hermione may have been docile; my guess is that Helen is trying to find out, at this very minute, whether she is or not."

"You may be right," said Menelaos. "I'd like to know where you learned so much about women."

"I know too much," said Eteoneus, "and in this house I'm constantly reminded of all I know. I ought to be in a place where I could forget some of it. I've been thinking over my retirement, as you suggested. Next week, when you're more at leisure, I'd like to come in and talk with you about it."

V

"Why, he's a perfect darling, Adraste! You're a fortunate girl. Let me take him—it's ages since I held one in my arms, but I still know how."

"You certainly do, Helen! There he goes, sucking his thumb again! Take it out, will you, Helen, please?"

"So you think you're going to break him of that habit?"

"Oughtn't I to try?"

"I suppose so—one learns so much in trying. Now that he has stopped being all red and has turned pink, I do believe he resembles you, Adraste. Do you see it?"

"Oh, no, Helen, I think he's much more like his father. I don't know whether to be glad or sorry."

"Be glad, of course. Damastor is very good-looking, and you'll want your boy to favor you both. But you can't form a final opinion when they are a week old. I dare say his mother has discovered some profound characteristics in him even now?"

"Do you know, I have, Helen. He's the best little companion—I know his ways already. And I imagine he begins to notice me a little. If he doesn't, I'll be jealous, for he certainly has his eyes fixed on you—from the moment you came in. You're used to that, of course."

"He is a darling!"

"Do you think they do know, so early, Helen?"

"Well, Hermione flirted with her father when she was

233

a week old. It's the only indiscreet thing she ever permitted herself to do. Of course they know, the moment they're born! Your boy grows wiser-looking every day. If he's to put on a more profound air than this, I shan't have the courage to face him. He is reading my soul at this minute. . . . There, poor child, don't cry! I'll give him back to you. There! What on earth are you crying about? I'm tiring you, to be sure . . . I'll come in again later, when you've had a chance to rest."

"Don't go, Helen, I'm not tired. Sometimes it comes over me—my dreadful fate; your kindness about the child makes me—"

"Nonsense!" said Helen. "You have no dreadful fate. You ought to be an extremely happy woman. You have this beautiful boy to love and bring up, and you have friends around you who are thinking how lucky the boy is in his mother. You'll give him a wonderful childhood, a wonderful youth; he will always be young and shining, like you."

"It's all very well to say cheering things—it's kind of you, Helen—but he will have only his mother; he won't have a father, like other boys—he won't have a complete home. I had no right to bear him, and all his life I shall be punished, seeing what he has missed."

"I doubt if nature considers our rights, one way or the other. As for his missing his father, in childhood and afterward, it's perfectly true, and I wouldn't try to gloss over the fact. I know, too, that you are grieving for the home you dreamed of having. Nobody could pretend you are as happy as you deserve to be. But even so, you ought to have peace of mind. Dear girl, it might be so much worse!"

"How possibly?"

"Why, he might have married you."

"You think that would have been worse!"

"Here, give me that baby again. He's much quieter with me, and I'll tell him some things he can profit by later. . . . Yes, much worse, considering Damastor's character. If he had been a great lover, the kind we invent but usually don't meet, the lasting kind, then to lose him would have been as tragic as you think it is—but then you wouldn't have lost him. He was a great lover at first, wasn't he! Only he couldn't keep it up. That's not his fault—nor yours; it's simply the way he is. You don't know what it would have been like to live with him, year after year, when he had ceased to be your lover and was drawing on his reserves of character to be your husband. Of course he would have been kind to you—you'd enjoy that, wouldn't you!—but even with him there, you'd find yourself deserted by the man you yearned for. A stranger, with a haunting resemblance to your lover—that's what you'd be living with. Now you are far better off. Not in the general opinion of society, but really so. The boy is the child of your love, and your love is fortunately bereaved, when it might have been tarnished or worn dull. Your sorrow, too, is bright and clean-cut. . . . Adraste, this young man will never like curtain lectures; he's going asleep. Shall I put him in his crib?"

"Please—and take his thumb out."

"It's all right—it's in again. . . . I think you're a lucky girl, Adraste, to have both your love and your sorrow pure."

"I don't see any luck in having sorrow, pure or impure."

"There isn't any luck in having it, but since we must have it, it's well to be able to feel it. That shows how alive, how essentially happy, you still are. I'd give a good deal to feel a sorrow. I mean what I say, I envy you. We've talked so often about love, you know what I think of that, and how widely I've missed my ideal there. In sorrow too I've missed it. Any one who sees how wonderful and how brief life is, would hope to know it, if not all of it, at least the high and deep things in it; the awful fate would be to be numb and sleepy, to rest in one's habits, to let the days simply pass. I wanted to know life down to the quick. Either it can't be done, or I never found out how. With me, life refuses to be known. It sets me apart, it makes me feel like a special case, and the normal fortunes I wanted—I'm convinced they are normal—seem dream-like."

"But, Helen, you always seem to me very wise in life. You told me the truth about Damastor long before I could see it, and you are kind not to remind me how I failed to take your advice. You couldn't know so much if you hadn't had more experience than you admit."

"That's the trouble; I think I do know about life, but not in the right way—not through my own feelings. Adraste, you understand I didn't come here to talk about myself! I'm trying to show you where I think you are less unfortunate than you believe. Since I haven't felt experience deeply in myself, I could only study others, try to understand life through them. When you learn to see human beings that way, and yourself, in spite of what they think, as just one more illustration of the common nature, you gain in charity, perhaps you acquire a more generous interest in your fellows, but the edge of sorrow is gone—indeed, of most passionate states. It isn't that you know too much; no one is too wise. But you forget how to cry, and you learn to smile at mankind, beginning with yourself. Love stays with us longer than sorrow, and pain stays longer; they both have somewhat to do with the body. But sorrow, the kind of heartache you have, seems all of the spirit. I'd rather my spirit had not been educated away from it."

"Helen, you make me sad, talking so. I have reason to know that your heart is tender, that you forgive quickly, that you are just even to—"

"I think I'm honest, my dear Adraste, but I have no other boast. The dark fact is that I have made many people unhappy, and I shall be remembered, if Menelaos or Hermione writes my obituary, as anything but generous or just. But I have one excuse, if I need one, for having come to see life as a comedy—a rather wistful and even sad comedy; at any moment in my later years I might have had a better reputation if I had been willing to renounce my virtues. If I had pretended a love for Menelaos which I no longer had, they would have called me a model wife. The tragedy really was in losing the love, but they think it was in admitting the fact. If I had pretended to be overwhelmed with repentance when I came home, nobody would have believed me, but they would have thought I was correct. Of course I felt no repentance. My love for Paris didn't prove to be the real thing, but it was the nearest to it I have known, and I am grateful to heaven for it. On the other hand, those who would reform me are not convincingly alive themselves, and though they have kept their reputations, they often seem to have mislaid their souls. The sorrows they

say they grieve over usually don't look like sorrows to
me—mere vexations or petty disappointments. They
don't know what sorrow is! I take that back—Orestes
knows. But Charitas, for example, thinks she has a sorrow because her boy wanted to choose his own wife. It's
rather funny, to call that a sorrow. And you think you
are overwhelmed because your lover wasn't a great man.
I say you ought to be grateful for the love that gave you
this child, and you ought to reflect on what you were
spared when Damastor permitted himself to be separated
from you. How awful if you had had to pretend you
were happy, after he had ceased to be what he once was.
You've had some of the real experiences, and few of us
have them all. You've had them unalloyed. Some of us
envy you. Don't let yourself think bitterly of your moonlight hours with him, of the glamour of his kisses, of the
ecstasy of his embrace. All that you felt then, was true.
People who laugh at such feelings have become incapable of having them. And don't you teach this boy that
love is dangerous and he ought to be careful, or that discretion is the secret of life!"

"I've thought a good deal already about the sort of
career I'd like him to have."

"You would, naturally. He's only a week old."

"But the responsibility is frightful, Helen."

"What responsibility is that?"

"Why, of bringing him up right."

"You'd better not try too hard. If I were doing it,
I'd remind myself that there is some natural goodness in
the human heart; then I'd look for it in the boy, and encourage it. He'll be fond of something, passionately interested in something, and the thing he cares for will be

innocent enough, at least while he's young. I'd simply encourage him. If he cares for nothing, he's hopeless. In that case I'd try to bring him up so that he'd do the least possible harm to the human race. I'd tell him that he has no right to reform people unless he loves the same things that they do. That would keep him out of mischief. But your boy will be like you and Damastor—yes, like his father; Damastor was weak, but for a time he was a lover. You'll want to protect the boy from the pressures that spoiled his father's soul. Think what a man Damastor would have been if his mother had encouraged him to lose his heart to the first pretty girl he met—if she had urged him to fall in love with the very prettiest, to dream of her, to hunt the world over for her!"

"In that case, of course, I shouldn't have had him, not even for a short time."

"Yes, you would. She ought to have told him it was his duty as well as his right to love you always. That kind of education would have made a difference in Damastor. . . . But I'll tell you something, Adraste— two things. When you have brought up your boy by this ideal method I'm suggesting, he won't turn out quite as you expect; he'll find some way of his own, and surprise you. And then you'll be a little false to your theories, and you'll feel a temptation to behave like Charitas. You'll say, 'My dear boy, I didn't bring you up to do so and so!' When that day comes, remember what I'm telling you; you'll understand that life is a comedy."

"I can't imagine him grown up—that pink and white innocence. Of course he'll have a will of his own—I want him to have that."

"Of course; you want him to have a will of his own,

and you'll ask him to do just as you say. Well, for the
time being he looks innocent. That's because we're so
much older, I dare say. The rest of it is probably illusion
except his feet. There's very little to be said for feet
after they've been used, but in children they are forms o
exquisiteness. Otherwise the healthy young seem beau
tiful to their elders, whether they are or not. It's a
strong reason for having an elder generation. There
you're looking tired again. I'm going now."

"Just a moment—please don't go. I've something
ought to say, if I'm to be frank, as you always urge us to
be. I do appreciate your cheery talk and the way you have
pretended that all is well with me. It's like you. But you
won't think me ungrateful if I detect the generous effor
in your remarks about life and youth and bringing up
children. This isn't the way we talked, give and take
when I was happy. Shall we ever be the same to each
other again? I know I'm not quite the friend I was; to
some extent I've become an object of pity. I owe it to you
that I have roof over me, this bed under me."

"Don't say such things, nor think them. You are
exactly as you were, one of my household, and partic
ularly dear to me."

"No, Helen, you can't deceive me. Menelaos wanted
to send me away."

"Of course he said so! Nothing could be more cor
rect. Nobody will ever be able to say that my husband
countenanced irregular behavior in his home. He said
you positively must go, and there was to be no more talk
There was no more talk, and you stayed. That's Mene
laos. He's really the kindest man who ever tried to keep
the world straight. He is willing to waive the results so

long as he can have an audience. The true reason why he brought me home instead of killing me, was that he wanted to save up some one to talk at in his old age. He never has said of you half the bad things he says to me, in the daily round. Neither he nor I can spare you; you will have to be the daughter of the house, now that Hermione is gone."

"Gone where? I haven't heard. Has she married Orestes?"

"She has left us—run away. I dare say she'll marry Orestes, if she hasn't done so already. Anyway, we have lost her. Her father threatened in an impulsive moment to arrange a match with Pyrrhus, and Hermione took him seriously, or pretended to. It gave her a first-rate excuse to throw herself on Orestes for protection. We don't know where she is."

"Don't you worry about her, Helen?"

"No, indeed! I grieve that we have not known how to get on better with our own daughter, but she is perfectly safe. What could harm her? I rather think her resolution to manage her own affairs will do her good. She has wasted some time trying to manage mine. If she isn't showing much filial respect for her father and me, on the other hand I'm not ready to argue that we deserve it. No, if this is the worst thing she does, I shall be content. . . . Adraste, has Charitas come to see her grandson?"

"She certainly hasn't, that old cat!"

"Speaking of filial respect! She's your mother-in-law, you know, in spirit if not in fact. Why don't you ask her to come?"

"I'd like to see myself! After the things she has said of me!"

"Exactly. Let her say them first, and then come. If I were you I'd ask her."

"She wouldn't come."

"Ask her. She'll say no. Tell her the boy waits to be seen, whenever she cares to look at him. She'll come. . . . And you might rescue Damastor that way."

"There! You said I was lucky not to marry him, and now you suggest getting him back!"

"It's a weakness in me, I admit. I think you would be quite perfect without him, but you don't, and you would never forgive me for not telling you how to get around his indignant mother. That's the way it's done. Now do as you like. Notice I said 'rescue' him. We want back the Damastor who perhaps doesn't yet exist. But he might. . . . Anyway, Adraste, I'm glad it's a boy. The girls do have the rough side, whenever there's a choice."

"Helen, do you think Hermione ought to marry Orestes?"

"My dear child, she's going to marry Orestes."

"But ought she to?"

"Do you mean, would I marry him? I'd drink poison just before the wedding. He's almost all that I don't like in human nature. He sees nothing good in life, but he consents to take charge of it."

"Helen, if Hermione marries and has a child, will you go see the child?"

"At once. I shan't wait to be invited. If they don't want me, they'll have to shut the door in my face. Why not?"

"But Orestes—and your sister!"

"The child won't be to blame. If Hermione marries,

I accept her choice. If she can accept it too, she'll be
fortunate. You know my rule—repent before, not afterward. And afterward it's really too late to criticize. Yes
indeed, we'll be looking across the same dinner table at
each other, Orestes and I, many a time, and he will medi-
tate on the immoral fact that my bad life doesn't affect
my appearance, while I wonder about the human conscience and its mysteries—how we are persuaded to do
detestable things for our own salvation and for the improvement of our friends."

"But, Helen, would you say of Hermione as you said
of me, that it would be better if her lover deserted her,
left her to bring up her child unmarried?"

"Dear me, I'm to be cross-examined! No, Adraste,
I'd never say the same thing of Hermione and of you. I
don't know that she could appreciate her opportunities if
Orestes deserted her. I'm not sure that either she or
Orestes is in love, ever was, or ever will be. The cases
aren't parallel. From what I can gather, they regard
each other not as lovers but as supreme obligations. To
Hermione certainly Orestes appeals as one of her duties.
If ever I have a word with him, I'll express my sympathy.
But I meant what I said, of your case, and I wish I could
say it of Hermione's; your problem is only with society—
and that's bad enough—but you have no quarrel with the
real things that count in the end."

"Will you put that rug over the baby? The air's
blowing on him."

"If he sleeps so soundly, he'll give you little trouble.
Oh, what a splendid rug!"

"What do you think? Eteoneus came in here, without
being invited, I assure you, and without asking permis-

sion, and he stormed around here like a wild man—said the house was going to the devil, and he must leave it, and he called me—the same thing as baggage, only worse, and said Damastor was an ass. Then he put this over baby and got out."

HELEN'S BEAUTY

I

"It simply comes to this," said Menelaos, "that we can't find her."

"That's it," said Eteoneus. "The men have been everywhere in the neighborhood, ten miles, I should say, in all directions, and no one has heard of her, or seen her go by."

"It's very strange that a young girl could walk out of a house in broad daylight, in a civilized country, and completely disappear!"

"My notion is that she didn't go far," said Eteoneus. "My idea isn't worth much, I confess, since I don't see how she could conceal herself near by, but if she came in at any moment I shouldn't be over-surprised."

"I should," said Menelaos. "She's looking for Orestes, and he's not in this part of the world."

"How do you know he's not?"

"He wouldn't have the impudence," said Menelaos.

"On the other hand," said Eteoneus, "it's all that you need for your most exquisite embarrassment, to have him show up just as Pyrrhus arrives. That's the kind of luck you've been having lately."

"That's not my worst embarrassment—the worst will be to welcome Pyrrhus with the news that my daughter has run away. We must find her—we must, Eteoneus.

I'm known to Pyrrhus chiefly as the man whose wife ran off, and if I must tell him my daughter has gone too—I can't face it, I simply can't!"

"It's too much to hope she's gone to welcome Pyrrhus. How she hates that man!"

"What do you propose to do next?" said Menelaos.

"I've come to the end. I have no suggestions."

"You must have, Eteoneus! We can't give up at this point."

"You needn't give up—you'll probably think of something. But I'm of no use to you, I fear; I haven't found a single trace of her, and to tell you the truth, my heart's not in it. While we were on this last search, I was wondering all the time what on earth to do with her if we found her."

"Bring her home! Those were your orders."

"Of course, but what then? I should think you'd rather tell Pyrrhus that Hermione happened to be out of town at the moment, than exhibit her in chains, or however you intended to hold her down. If she is brought back, it will be as a prisoner. You'd better let her go. It hurts me to think what we've come to, Menelaos. This is my last service for you, I suppose—trying to arrest your runaway daughter. I'll be glad when Pyrrhus comes, and I retire."

"I can't possibly spare you now till we find Hermione! You wouldn't think of leaving me before?"

"Well, Menelaos, I'd do anything in reason, but I'm very tired of my job, and I don't believe Hermione is ever coming back. You're asking me to stay for life."

"That's really what I'd like to ask you, but I mean only a reasonable time. Let's put it this way. Stay until

Hermione is found, whether she comes back here or not; the moment we know positively where she is, you may go. If she isn't found before Pyrrhus comes, stay until he goes. You think he is to arrive any day; the moment he leaves, you are free. That will see me through the worst in either case, and I'll prove to you that I know how to be grateful."

"I don't know," said Eteoneus. "It seems a little complicated. . . . Do you mean I may go the moment we know where Hermione is?"

"Exactly."

"Thank heaven, I can go now! What do you think of that! Here she is!"

"Where?"

"Right behind you—in the door."

"What does this mean, Hermione? Where have you been?"

"Ask that question some other time—it's irrelevant. I want to speak to you and mother."

"We have a word or two to say to you. I suppose you realize the annoyance your behavior—"

"Don't be silly, father! Where's mother?"

"Helen!—Oh, Helen! Hermione's here!"

"I suppose I may go now?" said Eteoneus.

"You needn't," said Hermione. "There's nothing in what I'm going to say you shouldn't hear. I'd rather like you to hear it."

"Hermione, dear child!" said Helen, "I'm glad indeed you came back to us."

"I haven't come back to you—I stopped in to tell you something, and when you hear it you won't be glad."

"Your absence hasn't improved your manners,"

said Menelaos. "You need have no fear of Pyrrhus if you talk to him as you do to your parents. He's a brave man, but he won't take that on for life."

"You still expect Pyrrhus to visit you?" said Hermione.

"Almost any time now."

"He isn't coming," said Hermione. "That's what I had to tell you."

"Not coming?" said Menelaos. "He accepted the invitation, and Eteoneus reported him on the way. How about that, Eteoneus?"

"He can't come now," said Hermione.

"Just as well, perhaps," said her father. "But I'd like to know why not?"

"He insulted Orestes."

"What's that got to do with it? Orestes doesn't choose our guests for us! What are you trying to tell us?"

"Orestes and I met Pyrrhus on the road, and—"

"What were you doing with Orestes?" said Menelaos.

"That's of no importance now," said Hermione. "He and I were walking together when we met Pyrrhus. I guessed who it was, but said nothing. He stopped to inquire the way, and before I could do anything to prevent it, they found out each other's name. Pyrrhus stiffened up at once, and said that as he was to be your guest, practically was your guest at the moment, he felt bound to offer me his protection. Orestes asked from whom he wanted to protect me, and Pyrrhus said, from a man who would lift his hand against his own mother. Before I realized what was happening, they had drawn their swords."

"They actually had a fight?" said Menelaos.

"I should say! Pyrrhus is dead."

"Hermione, Pyrrhus was my guest! Don't tell me Orestes killed a man coming to my house, on my invitation?"

"Orestes killed him, father, in the circumstances I have just reported."

"Now, that shows the idea of hospitality Orestes has," said Eteoneus. "I'll never again be sorry I kept him out. If there's a difference in such horrors, this is a bit worse than killing Clytemnestra. She at least had committed a crime herself."

"I shall never get over this!" said Menelaos. "If I could fall dead as I speak, I'd take it as a kindness of fate. I was none too friendly with Pyrrhus or his father. I asked him to visit me, and in good faith he came at once. Now one of my relatives met him on the way and killed him. What excuse can I give, to others or to myself?"

"Did Orestes know Pyrrhus was your father's guest?" said Helen.

"Yes," said Hermione.

"I owe it to Pyrrhus to find his body, and bury it handsomely," said Menelaos. "Then I suppose I ought to take vengeance on Orestes. If I don't, people will think me an accomplice in a trap for my former enemy."

"You can't take vengeance on Orestes!" said Hermione. "He did nothing wrong. I saw the whole thing, and had he done otherwise, I should despise him. Pyrrhus insulted him—I felt as though he were insulting me too. Don't misunderstand me—I'm not trying to defend Orestes; he doesn't need defense. It wasn't for my happiness, nor for any one else's, that Pyrrhus was coming.

I'm glad Orestes killed him. If he hadn't done it, I should.
I made up my mind to that, the day father told me he was
going to arrange a marriage. If you compel people to act
in self-defense, they'll act!"

"Clytemnestra!" said Menelaos.

"My conventional daughter!" said Helen.

"I see we've reached the end," said Menelaos. "If
any new catastrophe can overtake my house, at least I
don't know the name of it. There's nothing more to discuss; if Hermione wants Orestes after this, we'll have
to admit she knows the worst about him, and they say
there's no arguing in matters of taste. May I ask, Hermione, merely for information, if you dream of being the
wife of this murderer?"

"I don't dream," said Hermione, "I am."

"I thought so," said Helen.

"What did you say you were?" said Menelaos.

"His wife. I told you quite clearly I was going to
marry him. We weren't married when we met Pyrrhus,
and that was awkward, though the quarrel would not
have been avoided, probably, even if we had been. But I
showed Orestes that people would remark on our traveling together, when they spoke of the killing, and we ought
to marry at once. So we did."

"You may leave the house!" said Menelaos.
"Eteoneus, kindly open that door for her."

"Thank you, Eteoneus. I had no intention of staying
so long; I've been keeping Orestes waiting. Good-by!"

"One moment!" said Helen. "Menelaos, we have
reached the end, as you said. We have our opinion of
what Hermione and Orestes have done, but since they did
it on their own responsibility, we have no part in the con-

sequences. There's nothing more to be said, and we might as well be friends."

"I'll never be friends with Hermione and Orestes!"

"Of course you will! How absurd! Haven't you made a mistake, now and then? I have. It's all a question of degree. You get your punishment—or you don't, but it's not the business of your friends and your family to punish you. Do leave something to heaven, Menelaos! When a thing's once done, I like to begin afresh and go on with my life. If you try to be an avenging fate, you'll ruin your character. Orestes may be a criminal—that's his affair. But it looks to me as if he were in serious trouble, and Hermione too, since she has undertaken to share his fortunes. That really does concern you and me—we ought to help our children when they are in trouble."

"Orestes is no child of mine."

"Well, you're his nearest male relative, and the only person he can turn to. You needn't forgive his act—I don't; but we need never mention it again. You and I tried to provide well for Hermione, and we failed. Let's watch with a good will while she provides for herself. Hermione, so far as I'm concerned, this home is always open to you and your husband."

"It is not!" said Menelaos.

"You won't live here, of course," Helen went on; "it wouldn't be comfortable for you nor for us just now, and anyway, young people ought to have their own home. But when you wish to come to us, this is where you grew up, Hermione, and I dare say there is more love for you here than there ever will be anywhere else, no matter how popular you become."

"That's all right for Hermione," said Menelaos, "but it doesn't apply to Orestes. He didn't grow up here, and if he isn't more popular in some other place than he is here, he's a complete social failure. Make it clear to him, Hermione, that the family affection is limited to yourself; we won't receive him."

"If I may put it another way," said Helen, "I would suggest that we ask Hermione to send Orestes here at once. There ought to be no possibility of another misunderstanding in this home, and the wise way, I think, would be to talk it out with Orestes now. Don't send messages through Hermione or anybody else, Menelaos; talk to Orestes yourself."

"I won't permit him to enter the house—and naturally I won't talk with him."

"Then would you mind if I talked with him? It was my sister he killed, and if any one here is to blame for the death of Pyrrhus, it is I, who suggested his coming. I claim the right to speak with Orestes, Menelaos."

"I don't see what there is to say to him, Helen. He'll probably take the occasion to lecture you on your behavior, or he'll point out where I have done wrong."

"He may ask me why you didn't help him avenge his father," said Helen. "If he does, I'll explain that I kept you home. If he tells me that I have made mistakes, I'll admit it, and I'll fill in any gaps in his information about my past life. Orestes has no terrors for me, and I'm very eager to meet him. How soon can you get him here, Hermione?"

"Not here, Helen!" said Menelaos.

"The whole point would be lost if I met him anywhere else, and it would hardly be proper for me to be meeting

him out of my own house, and away from your protection,
Menelaos. How soon do you think, Hermione?"

"I prefer not to have him come, since father objects."

"Quite right," said Helen, "but your father has withdrawn his objection."

"I didn't know that I did."

"I beg your pardon! I thought you agreed it was
more discreet for me to see him here than alone and away
from the house."

"Oh, yes, in that sense," said Menelaos.

"Well, then, how soon do you think, Hermione?"

"I don't want him to come, mother. I'm not sure
what you would do to him."

"My dear child, he's entirely safe. My word of honor,
nothing will happen to him here."

"I don't know what you would say to him, and I
don't want him to see you," said Hermione. "He's perfectly happy now—or would be if it were not for his
private misfortunes."

"That's all that prevents any of us from being happy,"
said Helen, "except the few who worry over the misfortunes of others. You don't think Orestes is of that
kind. Send him here, Hermione. I promise to let you
have him again. Could he be here to-morrow?"

"You'd be wise to send him," said Menelaos. "It will
come to the same thing in the end. Your mother wants
to see him. I assure you I shan't let him stay long, and
we shan't do him any harm."

"Let me know when he's coming," said Eteoneus,
"and I'll tell the new gate-keeper to turn his back and
pretend not to notice him. You couldn't give a man like
that a formal hospitality."

"What's this about a new gate-keeper?" said Helen. "The old one is very satisfactory."

"Eteoneus is leaving us," said Menelaos. "He wishes to retire, and I promised to release him when Hermione returned. I never expected her so soon, or I wouldn't have promised. I have no one as yet to take his place."

"Couldn't you stay with us, Eteoneus?" said Helen. "You are my oldest friend here; you opened the door of this house when I entered as a bride."

"And when you returned from Troy," said Eteoneus. "There's nothing more I can do for you, and it's time I left."

"You mustn't leave—we'll have to talk it over," said Helen. "Your decision doesn't seem final to me."

"You'll stay, all right," said Menelaos. "I foresee the end."

"My decision is quite final, Helen, and I'd rather not discuss it at all."

"I'm sorry," said Helen, "but you know best. You will come in to say good-by to me before you go, won't you?"

"I certainly will," said Eteoneus.

"That does for you, old man!" said Menelaos. "And you're going to send Orestes in to-morrow, is that it?"

"No," said Hermione, "I'm not going to send him at all. I'm just waiting to say good-by myself to Eteoneus, and then I'm going. I shan't return. We're really not wanted here, and fine speeches won't alter the fact. I don't want to return, anyway—we never should agree."

"Go ahead, then, and leave!" said Menelaos. "Why are you hanging 'round to tell us, once in so often, you don't approve of us? Have you any sense at all of what you and your husband have done? Will any human being ever care whether or not you approve of him? We have permitted you to enter this home, and to stay in it a few minutes, just as though you were not an outcast. The next time you call on a friend, you'll probably feel the difference!"

"Menelaos! Menelaos!" said Helen. "I don't want Hermione to go until she has promised to send her husband to see us. If she will do that, I rather think we can some day understand one another again—all of us. It isn't my sister's murderer I want to talk with—it's her son. If Hermione loves him so desperately, there must be good in him I knew nothing about. I should like to admit my error, if it is one; I'd like to see for myself."

"He is a splendid man—you couldn't help admiring him, if you knew what he really is. The trouble with you and father was that you didn't know him, and you didn't want to."

"Of course we wanted to!" said Menelaos. "We told you to invite him for a visit, but you couldn't find him. It wasn't our fault that you didn't know where he was!"

"It wasn't Hermione's fault either," said Helen, "and we can see now that Orestes wasn't to blame. The fact is as you said, daughter—we don't know Orestes. Will you ask him to come to-morrow?"

"I'll give him the invitation," said Hermione. "I never know what he has to do."

II

"It was good of you to come, Orestes," said Helen. "I understand you are very busy at present, but I wanted to see you as soon as Hermione told us of the marriage."

"I'd like to say, but I can't, that I'm glad to come," said Orestes. "You have every reason to hate me. I dreaded to meet you."

"I don't hate you," said Helen, "and on your part I hope there is no occasion for dread. I should like to be friends with my daughter's husband; that's the whole reason why I asked you to come."

"You didn't want me to marry Hermione," said Orestes.

"I did not."

"You wanted her to marry Pyrrhus."

"I did."

"Then I'm not convinced of this sudden friendship."

"My dear Orestes, I always knew I should be on good terms with my son-in-law, when once he was selected. The friendship isn't sudden—the marriage was. I wish you could know how often your name has been mentioned in our house, since my return. I urged Hermione to invite you for a visit, we were so eager to meet you, but she didn't know where you were. You had our sympathy; we realized what terrible responsibilities you were shouldering. I'd like to tell you now, if I may, how deeply I sorrow for you."

"I feel like a hypocrite to accept your sympathy," said Orestes. "I haven't considered you a friend."

"How could you know I was? But I am—and may I count you one of my friends?"

"You can't very well. I recently killed your sister."

"I've heard that you did."

"And more recently I killed your guest, Pyrrhus."

"I've heard of that too."

"They are crimes of the worst sort, most people think."

"I think so too, my dear nephew, but it wasn't unfriendliness to me that made you commit them, was it? I thought you had other reasons."

"But surely you don't want to be friends with the man who killed your sister!"

"With the man who has married my daughter."

"I must say you are generous!"

"Not at all, it's only natural. Don't misunderstand me, Orestes; what you have done seems to me inexpressibly horrible. You'll pay a heavy penalty for it, in the treatment most people will give you, and still more in your own thoughts. I can't say how sorry I am for you. I should have done anything to prevent you from such a course, just as I tried to prevent Hermione from marrying you. But what's done is done, and we are now free to enjoy each other's friendship, and to sympathize with each other in the consequences of our mistakes. On my own behalf I grieve over what you have done; for your sake too. The better friends we are, the more I shall regret your actions. I didn't want Hermione to assume a share in your misery."

"I did not wish to lay any of it upon her, but she would have it so," said Orestes. "There is a kind of jus-

tice in it, since she is your child, for if we are talking of
our wrong-doing, I may as well say that I blame you for
the whole tragedy. My father presented his brother's
plea for your hand, and he always felt an obligation to
see Menelaos safely through the dangers of his brilliant
marriage. That's how it all began—with your beauty.
Agamemnon sacrificed his daughter to get the fleet
started. I think my mother was justified in leaving him,
after that. She felt she ought to avenge her child by
killing him, if he should return. She wasn't clear as to
her duty—for that reason she did not pursue him, but if
he came back she was resolved to punish him. She was
wrong, I am sure, but I respect her motives. That is why
I found it so terribly hard to avenge my father—but of
course I had no choice. Now I have quarreled fatally
with your guest. Iphigeneia—Agamemnon—Clytemnestra—Pyrrhus. That is the sanguinary logic of your behavior. My mother felt you were to blame. She said
you were inordinately beautiful. You are. But she said
also that wherever you came, people began to do wrong.
I can see that would be so. Can you sleep soundly? I
can't. But what I have done seems, I suppose, amateur-
ish and unimportant to you. That's why you can greet me
so cheerfully. You have caused so many men to do awful
things, who except for you would have led uneventful and
innocent lives. All those men dead at Troy—their children slain or starved—the women captured and disgraced! We can never be very good friends; I couldn't
bring myself to enjoy the sight of your loveliness while
I knew the evil effects it had produced."

"We shan't quarrel over your opinion, Orestes," said
Helen. "It is essentially my own opinion. It's what I

expected you to think of me. Where I have been, disaster has always followed. If it had not been for me, your father would not have offered up his own child, my sister would not have slain her husband, you would not have killed your mother, nor Pyrrhus—and you wouldn't have married Hermione."

"Oh, I should have married Hermione anyway! That's not a catastrophe, and you are in no way responsible for it. I married Hermione because I love her."

"That is usually thought to be a good reason," said Helen. "I dare say your union was foreordained—you would have married her no matter how admirable her mother was."

"Yes—no! I mean, when you love as Hermione and I do, you can not help yourself."

"You never met Paris, did you? Of course not. He felt the same way about it."

"And you didn't agree with him, I suppose?"

"Yes, I did."

"Then you've changed your mind since?"

"No, I still believe it. That's why I'm glad to know it was love that drove you into matrimony. I was afraid it might have been Hermione. She made no secret of her intention to have you."

"Oh, you must not do her such an injustice! We—"

"What injustice have I done her?"

"You implied that she forced me to marry her."

"Didn't she? I thought you said you couldn't help it? Was it her charm or yours that overwhelmed you?"

"Oh—in that sense."

"Of course, I'm unfair," Helen went on. "It was your charm that compelled her."

"I don't pretend to any charm," said Orestes.

"Well, whatever it was, Paris found the same thing in me, and I found it in him. Isn't it strange how love becomes our will! We couldn't have done otherwise."

"Oh, I beg your pardon! Such a theory would make your passion for that Trojan rascal as sacred as any other love!"

"I didn't mention any theory," said Helen. "I was citing a fact. You told me how you and Hermione felt; I told you how Paris and I felt. Why did you call him a rascal? You didn't know him. Our love was decidedly like any other love; it seemed to us sacred. If you prefer, I'll cite a parallel from Menelaos. When he married me he too said he couldn't have done otherwise. Now he thinks he could, and he wishes he had. But at the time he was right."

"If you could not have done otherwise," said Orestes, "you are logically not to blame for the miseries that followed. It's an ingenious point of view, but I don't think it will hold. Who is responsible for it all?"

"I've often wondered," said Helen, "but I still don't know. I could make an argument to show it was Menelaos' fault, but then I should have to explain Menelaos, and the deeper you get in, the more difficult it is. That is why I have learned to accept a thing once done, as done; we must take the consequences, but there's no sense in debating it as though it were still to do, and I am disinclined to pass judgment on the doer."

"That's a most upsetting doctrine! That would leave all wrong-doers unpunished!"

"Never—unless you feel there is nothing ethical in life itself. I still like to believe you can find out whether an

action is right or wrong by doing it—that a right action
has better results."

"Of course, in general," said Orestes. "But in the
practical world, in society, you've got to distinguish between criminals and others."

"I'd like to," said Helen, "but I doubt if any one
can—that is, not until you have a long time to watch the
result of their lives. Take yourself, for example: I don't
know whether you are a murderer or an unusually
dutiful son."

"I tried to do my duty," said Orestes, "but what I did
makes me fiendishly unhappy."

"Exactly," said Helen. "You are probably something of both—I meant to say, your deeds were both bad
and good. You acted from the highest motives you had,
but maybe they weren't high enough. Your morals are
beyond criticism, but perhaps your information was inadequate. I notice that most people feel they may safely
act when they know they are right. It strikes me, after
a few experiments, that when we are sure we are right
we had better be careful. We've probably overlooked
something. In love, as you say, we can't help ourselves—
I'm referring to everything else. Your father had what
seems to me—seemed so at the time, when I heard of it—
an obsolete faith in sacrifices. A god, to him, was a being from whom you bought what you wanted. With the
clearest conscience, therefore, he sacrificed his daughter
in the hope of securing a favorable wind. Your father
and my husband were the poorest sailors I ever met.
Menelaos steered right into Egypt, trying to get home to
Sparta. I got him to make some sacrifices himself, finally. They were good for his stubbornness and pride,

whether or not they affected the wind. Pride is a worse sin than your father was guilty of, yet the consequence of his sacrifice was more terrible. It's puzzling to me. You think I did wrong in going to Troy, though you understand, I'm grateful to know, that I couldn't have done otherwise. But I dare say you think Menelaos was compelled to bring on a great war, destroy a city, take hundreds to their death, all because his wife ran away. You think I'm to blame. Well, I don't see it. I think it was pride and a lack of imagination. He, not I, caused all those deaths, though he acted with a clear conscience and is rather satisfied with himself, and I knew I was doing a tragic thing, though I couldn't help it. Which of us is really responsible for the suffering that followed? I think a decent man could lose his wife without bringing on a war."

"Don't you think a wife should be punished for deserting her husband?"

"It depends upon the wife and the husband," said Helen. "I should have to know the special case you refer to."

"I was thinking of you," said Orestes.

"Perhaps I should be punished—perhaps I am punished, but not by Menelaos. He got his friends to destroy Troy and let themselves be killed, but here he and I are back again. I know he feels he accomplished something, and I think it best not to ask him what."

"Why not?"

"For the same reason that I should not ask you what you accomplished when you punished your mother, or what she accomplished when she killed your father. It's kind to ask people only their intentions; if we saw the true meaning of what we have done, perhaps we couldn't survive."

"You confuse me terribly—you can't know how terribly!"

"Yes, I can," said Helen. "I did it deliberately. You came here thinking me a bad woman, and yourself something of a martyr to duty. You were right about yourself; you are a martyr to what you thought was your duty. So was your mother. But after what I have said, you are not so sure. You probably continue to think me bad, but you see that it might not be so easy to prove, if we came to an argument about it. About my own conduct, Orestes, I have long been confused. But I won't hang my head over anything I've done. I'll take what retribution life has for me; if it has none, I'll be thankful that what I did isn't so bad as I feared."

"That's a terribly dangerous doctrine," said Orestes.

"I'm not trying to convert you to it," said Helen. "I merely wanted to explain myself, and perhaps to comfort you a little. Some of the wrong we do is crime, and some error; our mistakes ought to be less tragic than our sins, but it often turns out the other way. You, I think, have made some terrible mistakes, but that won't interfere with our friendship. Of course I do hope you won't repeat them."

"What you say sounds kind and I'm grateful for it, but it still seems immoral," said Orestes.

"Perhaps it is," said Helen. "It's the best I can do. At any rate, there are no hard feelings between us?"

"I don't approve of your visit to Troy, and all that," said Orestes, "but that's past."

"I'm afraid it is," said Helen.

"That doesn't sound like repentance," said Orestes.

"I hope it doesn't," said Helen.

"Menelaos may have some hard feelings toward me, if you haven't," said Orestes. "Queer I didn't think of that before! It's no use for us to be reconciled, if he continues vindictive."

"He's not vindictive," said Helen. "He's all for punishing the wicked. The two things may look the same, but they're not. At present he wouldn't even speak to you, but in time he'll get around to it. He rather admires you—you were his favorite suitor for Hermione, from the first."

"Hermione told me so. She thought her father was very much on her side, but lately she has felt that he—well, she said he betrayed her."

"Hermione must get over thinking that people have betrayed her when they only disagree with her. Do you think you and she can get along, after all this excitement has died down?"

"Of course we can—the excitement, as you call it, has been no aid to our love."

"Oh, don't you think so?" said Helen. "Hermione wants to help you. You've got to keep on needing help."

"I think you misunderstand our relation," said Orestes. "We are born companions. I was glad to marry her."

"Poor boy, was that all?"

"I mean, I hoped we could marry soon, but I saw no prospect of giving her the home she deserves—they won't let me go back to my father's estate. After that ghastly quarrel with Pyrrhus, I realized at once that Hermione would be compromised in the scandal if she were not my wife. In fact, it was her usual good sense that saw the point first, but as soon as she urged it, I knew she was right, and I was glad for her sake to marry without delay—though, of course, it wasn't the moment you'd choose for a wedding."

"She's very much like Clytemnestra," said Helen.

"You don't know how I hate to hear you say that!" said Orestes.

"I beg your pardon!" said Helen. "It was worse than tactless."

"The trouble is," said Orestes, "I've noticed the resemblance myself, and at a most unfortunate moment. When I struck Pyrrhus down she was glad. I never saw such a look on another face—but one. It has haunted me to so painful a degree that I wonder whether my mind has not been ruined by what I've gone through. If I'm to see my mother and my father and Pyrrhus in the faces of those about me—if all this blood is going to poison the least taste of happiness— Oh, you can't guess how horrible it is! And I can't talk to Hermione about it, because it concerns her, and besides, she wouldn't entirely understand; she doesn't seem to have any misgivings about what she does. You're the one person to whom I've spoken, and when I came I had no idea of confiding such a thing to you."

"I am glad you did, Orestes—proud to have your confidence. If it is a sign of a ruined mind to see a resemblance to Clytemnestra in Hermione, my mind has been ruined for a long time. She has her aunt's positive feeling on any subject she notices at all; there's no light and shade to Hermione. I can think of her as marrying a man or murdering him, but nothing in between. Her adverse judgments are severe. One of my girls in the house was recently betrayed by a scandalously mean lover, and when we found that she would have a child, Hermione wanted her dismissed in disgrace."

"Hermione told me about that," said Orestes. "I must say I agreed with her entirely. There are limits to broad-mindedness."

"I have always found that there were," said Helen. "You and Hermione must work out those things for yourselves, but you are right in thinking she is like your mother. I never could see that she resembled me."

"Not in the slightest!" said Orestes.

"She does resemble her father in some ways," Helen went on, "and I hope you will do what you can to bring those two together again. Menelaos is devoted to her— she is the person he loves best in the world; it's often so with fathers and daughters. Menelaos tried to discourage her from marrying you, and she took offense. Since you have won her, you can afford to be generous and reconcile them. It wouldn't be a good thing for her or for him to go on through the rest of their days cherishing a grudge."

"She told me about it," said Orestes, "and of course I shall want to do whatever is right, but I must say the things Menelaos chose to slander me with are not easy to forget. He has a hasty temper, Hermione tells me, and once he has taken a position, he is stubborn. Hermione deplores that trait in him, as the chief cause of their sad relations. I don't see at the moment how I can interfere. If Menelaos is in the wrong, he ought to make the first advances. I certainly can't apologize for the unpleasant remarks he made at my expense."

"Perhaps the situation is impossible," said Helen. "Forgive me for mentioning it. But you may be able to approach Menelaos—or Hermione, whichever you think best—and effect an understanding. If you can't do it, nobody can. I have faith in your wisdom."

"It is difficult, as you say, but of course I'll do my best," said Orestes.

III

"I've come to say good-by, father. Orestes and I start to-morrow."

"I'm sorry, Hermione—I don't want to lose you. And going off with that—"

"Don't say anything against him, father! You'll understand him better, perhaps, some day."

"That won't be a reason for liking him better. Just where are you going on your wedding-trip—or is it a secret?"

"We don't know exactly. To Delphi, Orestes says, but that doesn't sound interesting to me. The main thing is, he needs a complete change. We'll hit on some place that suits us both."

"When are you coming back?" said Menelaos.

"We haven't the remotest idea, but it won't be soon. Orestes can't stay home, of course, and we both of us need to see the world."

"Well, you know what I think of it all," said Menelaos. "You'll probably starve, or you would if you hadn't something to fall back on besides your husband. I've asked Eteoneus to put together some food and some treasure; one of the men will carry it wherever you tell him to."

"Thank you, father, but I can't take it. Orestes will provide very well, I'm sure."

"He hasn't a thing in the world," said Menelaos, "and he has no friends now."

"Even if that is so, I can't take your gift," said Hermione. "Unless you have changed your mind and will receive Orestes."

"I'll never speak to him!" said Menelaos.

"You see why I can't take it. Good-by, father."

"You can do this at least," said Menelaos. "If ever you are in serious trouble, let me know. There's no point in your going without when your mother and I have plenty."

"You'll never hear from me again," said Hermione, "unless you accept my husband."

"Isn't it enough for you to marry him?" said Menelaos. "Must I love him too?"

"You know very well what I mean; unless you treat Orestes like a normal son-in-law, and not like a criminal, I can not consider myself any longer a member of this family."

"Well, there's nothing to say, then. Good-by. Tell Eteoneus, as you go out, to unpack those things and put them back in the cellar."

"Oh, there's one thing I meant to say, and I almost forgot," said Hermione. "I think you're a little hard on mother."

"Hard on your mother, did you say? Since when?"

"Ever since you came back—though I realized it only recently. You misjudge her, and you say things to her that might be interpreted as criticism. A person as sensitive as she is must find her position at times uncomfortable. I hope, for your sake and hers, you'll try to get her point of view."

"I had no idea the curse worked so quickly!" said Menelaos. "You've lost your mind."

"Don't worry about that curse, father—it isn't going to come off. I've still the same mind I inherited, and you used to say I took after you. Mother and I disagreed about Orestes, and in general she and I are quite different, but I'm just beginning to see her quality. There's nothing little about her. She's magnanimous."

"I never heard such nonsense in my life, and if you still have your wits about you, Hermione, you won't try to tell me that I've been less than generous to your mother. She's the magnanimous one, is she?"

"I didn't mean to set up a contrast between you," said Hermione, "but only to speak of her large-mindedness. Since you mention it, however, there was a contrast on the occasion when I first noticed this remarkable trait in her. You know how she always says to do your criticizing in advance, and afterward drop it? I had no idea she would live up to that if she had to do the forgiving. But when we learned that Orestes had killed her sister, did you notice how quickly she pulled herself together, and refused to expel Orestes from the family circle?"

"A parable for my benefit, eh?" said Menelaos. "It's clever—I see your brain is still working, daughter, but so is mine. Orestes is outside the family circle, so far as I'm concerned. I've my own opinion of your mother's magnanimity."

"May I hear what it is?" said Hermione. "I can't imagine anything finer than such a prompt reaching out of kindness to a person who had brought so great a sorrow on you. It's the first time I saw the unselfish side of mother; perhaps I've been overlooking the other occasions when she was equally generous."

"They haven't been many, even granting this one,

which I don't. You say I fail to understand your mother. You're quite right. The only thing about her I understand is her looks, and I don't understand how they last so well. To my eyes, she never has been so splendid as during these weeks, when heavy blows have fallen on her. She was the same way that night at Troy. Her beauty can rise to a critical moment!"

"Of course she's very handsome," said Hermione, "but it was of her character I was speaking."

"I'm coming to her character now," said Menelaos. "I spoke of her beauty first, as being of some importance. I'm really not sure she has any character; I wonder if she has a heart. Do you know—I can speak to you more intimately about your mother, now you're married—do you know I never saw your mother excited about anything. She says she was passionately in love with Paris—passionately! I wish I could have seen her in the state of mind she describes. Before she ran off with him, she was treating him with that calm detached sort of courtesy she has for almost anybody; each time she began to speak to him, I was worried with the fear that she had forgotten his name. Imagine how I felt when she went off with him! And imagine how I feel when she talks to me—to me, in that brazen way of hers—about the passion she had for Paris! She's a very selfish person, I say. Always determined to be frank! Who wants her to be frank? You'd think she was yielding to a public demand. Now, this wish to send for Orestes at once. What reason had she for fancying he wished to come?"

"Father, I'm the last one to say mother treated you kindly, or behaved properly. I meant only that she has a magnanimous side I hadn't noticed, and perhaps you haven't noticed it either. She can allow for a different point of view, and she's not stubborn. You are, father, a little bit, you know, and perhaps that's why you don't get on better with her."

"I don't know what Orestes would say if he heard this talk," said Menelaos, "but it bodes no good for him. He may prove to be as forgiving a husband as I have been, but will he get the slightest credit for it? No! They'll say that you are magnanimous!"

"Father, are you getting mixed in your figures of speech, or do you really expect me to duplicate mother's career? Not even Orestes thinks I have the equipment. Since he saw mother, he has praised me for everything but my looks."

"But he hasn't seen her since he was a baby!"

"He saw her two days ago—had a very satisfactory talk with her. That's awfully fine when you come to think of it; his mother was her sister, yet she was positively sympathetic, Orestes said, and didn't upbraid him, nor imply that he was beyond mercy, not a syllable of that kind. Orestes confirmed my impression that with all her faults, she's a very remarkable woman."

"Again I get your meaning," said Menelaos. "If Helen, with a greater grief, can forgive Orestes and treat him cordially, why can not Menelaos, who after all lost no relative by the sword of Orestes—only an unwelcome guest. Well, there's room for only one remarkable person of that kind in this family. I give way to Helen."

"You really are mistaken," said Hermione. "Of course you think I am speaking for Orestes, but really it's for you. Orestes and I are going on a journey, and whether or not you appreciate him is only a matter of sentiment with me. But I'd like to feel that you and mother were entirely happy again—my own happiness makes me wish that for mother—and I begin to see that the chief obstacle is your lack of—"

"Do you realize how impertinent you are?" said Menelaos. "What business is it of yours whether or not your mother is happy with me? And how would you know whether I understood her? You have been at swords' points with her yourself, so far as I could see, until this very moment, and I believe you haven't the temperament to see things her way, even if you cared to. You must remember I've been rather intimate with Helen and her doings for a longer time than you've been alive; she's almost an intuitive habit with me now. I understand her all right. Don't worry. If she isn't happy it's her own fault. I suppose you still admit she has faults?"

"What are they, father? She is human, of course, but I'd like to hear you name the things you would like to change. Her appearance?"

"We'll discuss her character," said Menelaos. "I just told you I believe she has no heart. She can do anything at all, or have the most tragic things happen to her, and not be disturbed in the slightest. She's without feelings. Then I might as well say I think her utterly immoral. Almost every sin has a bright side for her. If she elopes from her home and gets caught and brought back, she says 'My mistake!' and goes on as though nothing had happened, and she doesn't always say it's her mistake. That's the magnanimity you are praising. She has had so much practise forgiving herself, she can forgive anybody now."

"I knew you didn't understand. Have you ever thought of sitting down and talking with her about her philosophy of life? It would be illuminating. Orestes said this morning that if he hadn't heard her talk on the subject of his own troubles, he would never have caught the angle from which her conduct can be understood."

"I've said so much against your husband, Hermione, that I'm reluctant to imply anything further, but strictly with reference to your mother I'll confess I'd have to commit a few murders before I could catch that angle. Your mother's philosophy would do me no good, if she has one, but I suspect she moves from point to point in her life without a settled plan."

"Orestes says she made such an interesting distinction between sin and error."

"Oh, that!" said Menelaos. "That part of her philosophy we work out frequently. She makes all the mistakes and I commit all the crimes."

"No, seriously—she told him that her calmness, what you call her coldness, is simply her resolve to take the consequences of any action once it is done. Our marriage, for instance; she said frankly that she disapproved while it was debatable, but now it was over, she wished us joy and wanted to be friends. She told Orestes to look on his own experiences the same way. If he had done his best, he should have no regrets, not even if the consequences proved he had done wrong. You see she is too proud to go around saying she is sorry; she prefers to accept the punishment, if there is any—and usually, she says, there isn't."

"I don't believe she's sorry at all—you've got that wrong, but I believe she's too proud. As for the rest of it, I don't get it very clearly. Orestes liked the doctrine, did he?"

"I wouldn't quite say that. He thinks it's dangerous unless carefully applied. But he has said several times that he'd like to talk with her again about it, and he believes he could clarify the ideas for her, and take the danger out, in a little quiet conversation. If he can, why can't you?"

"Because I'm her husband," said Menelaos. "Are you going to let him continue those ethical discussions?"

"There may not be time until we come back, and that will be, as I said, not soon. But he is hoping to see her to-morrow before we go. He thinks as I do, that you can not have seen the possibilities in her character."

"Hermione, keep your husband away from her! He's simply another victim. That woman has only one career—to be fascinating. She'd rather have Pyrrhus than Orestes, but Orestes will do. The upshot will be that he will become discontented with you—you see if he doesn't! I dare say she told him she greatly admired his ideas, or something, and flattered the fool. Those tricks no longer deceive me, that's why I'm disqualified for any little chats with her about the philosophy of life."

"Mother isn't flirting with Orestes, if that's what you mean. Orestes is not the easily flattered kind. And she didn't say she admired him—only that she was sorry for him. He thought her whole position showed remarkable self-respect."

"She has that," said Menelaos. "Did your husband say he thought she was extremely beautiful?"

"No, only that she was far handsomer than he had been led to expect."

"You see—he's cautious with you already! Don't let him see her again, Hermione. It has happened too often for me to mistake the symptoms. He will talk to her for her good, and she will listen in the most docile flattery, and she won't say a word that isn't correct, but he will never get over it. He'll dream of her waking and sleeping, and in her honor he may finally throw away his life, as Paris did, though I doubt if she elopes with any more of them. You think you have a good husband. I begin to see that keeping him out of this house was a kindness to you. If you only had shielded him from Helen!"

"If there is any real danger," said Hermione, "I wish I had thought of it in time. It's easier not to get Orestes started than to stop him afterward. I thought, of course, it would be to his advantage to see mother, since she suggested it. You remember I didn't like the proposal at first, and then I had to persuade him to go. But he certainly is ready to go the second time. How do you think I had better divert him?"

"Get him away if you can," said Menelaos. "If you begin telling him not to admire her, he'll guess that you're jealous. I wish I could tell him a few things!"

"Wouldn't he suspect that you were jealous then?" said Hermione. "And you wouldn't talk to another man about your wife, would you? I come back to my first view—you do mother an injustice. If you would talk to her about herself in a cordial and sympathetic way—and it ought to be very easy to be at least as sympathetic and cordial as Orestes was when he went—you would be sensible of her appeal, quite aside from the sort of charm that causes you to be jealous. Don't waste time talking to Orestes—talk to her. Last night, when he happened to be on the subject, Orestes made a wise remark, I thought; he said he imagined that some married people have never exchanged ideas with each other to the same extent as with their casual neighbors, because most marriages begin irrationally, in passion, and since there's no connection between passion and intelligence, when the passion fades they don't know how to proceed to the other form of discourse. I thought that was clever, don't you? It made me glad that he and I came together through—well, you might call it conviction, rather than a less worthy kind of attraction."

"Hm!" said Menelaos. "Your mother would say that passion is a form of intelligence. When she gets on that love-of-life talk, she makes me uncomfortable because I half think she means I don't love her enough. If I loved her as she imagines she deserves, she'd say I had all the love of life necessary. I never meant to say this to any one, but I'd feel relieved to put it into words. When I first met her, she was no more beautiful than she is now, I dare say, but she had the added effect of novelty; you couldn't conceive of such a person if you hadn't seen for yourself. When she chose me, I won't say I felt as though it were a dream, or anything of that sort; I just felt that she had made a mistake. The other suitors would have felt the same way. I couldn't persuade myself that I belonged to that loveliness. When we were safely married and I took her home, and we were supposed to be settling down to a normal existence, I was pretty much in torment; I wanted her, I had got her, and she always seemed to be contemplating me as you might an infant, half amused; it seemed as though she were saying to herself, 'He wants to worship this beauty!

Well, let him go ahead and worship. But he's not quite
up to it, poor child!' The fact is, Hermione, I wasn't up
to it, and I never have been. I can't do without her, and
I don't know what to do with her. Ordinary beauty
calls for human embraces, in the love we are accustomed
to speak of, but the men who have had Helen in their
arms have all been baffled and humbled; you can't embrace a stream of music, or light on the sea. You needn't
tell me—I know she has craved a lover who would be her
equal, but there is none. In my heart I forgave her long
ago, especially since Paris was no more of a success than
I. The reason I didn't kill her that night was that when
I saw her there she seemed younger than ever, and
strangely virginal; and it came over me that in the sense
in which I have been speaking, nobody, not even I, had
ever loved her, and since I had failed, there was no point
in punishing her. Of course, she was looking her best
that night, too. But the moment we had words, I began
to be irritated with her, as I was before Paris came. She
is so inaccessible, she makes me feel so inadequate, she is
so close to laughing at me most of the time. . . . Well,
this is more than I intended to say. You may forget it
at once. Whatever you do, don't repeat it to Orestes.
But you see, I understand your mother from my point of
view, and since you have hers, as you think, you might as
well have mine. We shan't be different now, not in any
marked respect. She will be lovelier as she grows older,
and I dare say I shall be more irritable."

"You really are in love with her, aren't you?" said
Hermione. "She's not nearly so beautiful as you think
her."

"I ought to have said," Menelaos went on, "that the

full quality of her charm has never been discernible to her own sex. The instinct of self-preservation, I suppose."

"Do you know," said Hermione, "since you have confessed so much, I'll admit that I'm jealous of mother. I mean, I'm afraid that her charm will upset Orestes. You've convinced me! I wish you'd help me, father!"

"I'll do anything I can."

"Then I've an idea—see Orestes to-morrow! If you'll see him and forgive him in the hour he would have spent with mother, I'll look after him from then on!"

"Of course this isn't a neat little plot!" said Menelaos. "You never intended to work me into a position where I'd have to receive your husband! Oh, no!"

IV

"Your going is a special grief to me," said Helen, "because I fear I'm partly the cause of it. I shouldn't want you to leave us anyway, but it's worse if it's personal. I'm not accustomed to have people leave me."

"When Menelaos brought you home," said Eteoneus, "I told him I was too old to take up with new ideas, and perhaps I ought to retire. The new ideas I referred to were some of Hermione's and her husband's. Ever since, I've tried to find out where I stood. Sometimes I could follow what you were all doing and saying, sometimes I couldn't. It has been very wearing. When I wake in the morning now, I catch myself groaning and saying, instinctively, 'My God, must I get up to it again!' and at night when I go to bed my pulse isn't steady—I'm all in a flutter. It's time I got out."

"It must have been a frightful ordeal for you in the last weeks," said Helen. "I shall never be able to thank you enough for your loyalty to us while we were in deep trouble. But it's over now, don't you think? If you stay with us, we can promise you quiet as last."

"Isn't somebody going to kill Orestes?" said Eteoneus. "That's logically the next step."

"Perhaps, but I believe he is safe. After all, he and Pyrrhus had a perfectly open fight, and the popular version is that they fought over Hermione. You know how people feel about such things—they don't take revenge on the man who wins the woman, not after a fair fight.

I don't see much sense in it all—the fighting or anything else, but that's the way they do it. I quite understand your reluctance to report more of such adventures—the murder of Orestes, for example."

"Now that he has married Hermione," said Eteoneus. "If they had cut him down before, I could have stood it. But the difficulty isn't in that sort of adventure; it's in the general atmosphere of the home. When you married Menelaos and came here, I could see at once that something was going to happen. The presentiment grew each year, until you finally ran away. That was a great relief to me, not because I disliked you, but because it cleared the air; I knew just where we stood. Menelaos would go after you, I would guard the house, he would return finally, and whatever our grief, we should go on again normally from that point."

"You are quite right," said Helen. "I should have died at Troy."

"I don't like to say that," said Eteoneus, "but you see for yourself! Now we are back where we were when you first arrived. There is no prospect of a solution, I should say."

"I have an idea the solution has been found without our help," said Helen. "We have been concerned about Hermione's future. Any uneasiness of mind which the household have felt on that score, should be blamed entirely on me. I deserted Hermione when she needed my guidance. Since my return I've seen clearly what she lost by my absence, and I'm only sorry I can't bear all the annoyance of her behavior myself. As for my love of Paris, I maintain it was unavoidable, and I have no regrets for it. Deserting my daughter was another matter."

"It would be hard to keep the two episodes apart, I should think," said Eteoneus. "Do you mean that if you fell in love with another visitor to the same extent, you would run away again?"

"Certainly," said Helen.

"I'll leave now while it's quiet," said Eteoneus. "I couldn't go through it all again, I simply couldn't."

"If you stayed, you might protect me," said Helen. "You know how to protect my husband's interests better than any man he's likely to find. Very probably I shall never fall in love again, nor any one will lose his heart to me."

"I wouldn't put the slightest faith in that. I didn't blame Paris," said Eteoneus. "In a way, I didn't blame you, since, as you say, you were infatuated with the fellow. All that was natural enough, and I knew what to think of it. And besides, I could see that Menelaos didn't understand you. He's had no experience at all with women."

"He may not have understood me then, but he has no difficulty now. That's not the trouble with Menelaos. He's too soft, I'd rather say. He never lives out his wisdom. He knows far more than he knows what to do with, as to me and other things."

"That's exactly what I've been trying to say!" Eteoneus exclaimed. "I had no idea you saw it too."

"Why, Eteoneus," said Helen, "you and I have more ideas in common than any other two people in the house. We have had some experience of the world, and we've thought about what we have seen. I shall miss you terribly if you leave us. You could help me from now on— as indeed you have been helping. I haven't had the opportunity before to thank you for what you said to Hermione."

"About women?"

"Yes."

"Why, Menelaos was going to put me out of the house for that!"

"He would feel that way about it," said Helen, "but you told the truth. And Hermione needed to hear it. I suspect Menelaos knew it was the truth, too. And from the first you did the right thing about Orestes. And you showed a human attitude toward poor Adraste. You are really a very noble man!"

"I'm a very ordinary one," said Eteoneus, "and I'm not what I was. It is kind of you to speak so—in fact, it's the first compliment I've had from anybody since you went to Troy. I don't count the tributes I could pick out of your husband's sarcastic remarks if I tried."

"Oh, he likes you enormously, Eteoneus! I rather fancy he relies on you to see that his more foolish commands are not carried out. If he gets a new man who obeys him literally, the house will be ruined. Won't you stay?"

"If you both want me so badly—" said Eteoneus. "But there are other difficulties, too. I'd better go now, before we get in deeper."

"Let me hear the other difficulties," said Helen. "Perhaps we could reach some solution of them."

"Hermione and Orestes," said Eteoneus. "We're not through with them. They think they want to travel indefinitely, but what's indefinitely? Menelaos forgave Orestes before they left, and he's wrapped up in his daughter—"

"He should be," said Helen.

"Oh, I know," said Eteoneus, "but they will come back, that's the difficulty. When Menelaos forgave him, it was on the assumption that they were saying good-by forever. First I had to get that food and stuff done up in bags for Hermione, then I had to put it away because she was too proud to accept it, then I had to get it all out again the next day, and twice as much, for Orestes. He wasn't too proud, I can tell you. And Menelaos made him promise, without any great difficulty, that if ever Hermione was in need, they'd let us know. We'll be feeding them at a distance till they find it more convenient to be fed near by."

"Orestes will go back to his father's estate after a while," said Helen. "There's no doubt at all that the very people who are critical of him now will want him to rule them later. Then he will have the best of homes for his wife."

"Do you think he would care to settle down and look after his own affairs?" said Eteoneus. "Remember he has grown up in a hide-and-seek kind of existence, at first eluding his mother, then hunting Ægisthus, then waylaying Pyrrhus. I fancy he is too much accustomed to it to change. If he only could take vengeance on himself for Pyrrhus, he'd be entirely in the vein. But I can't imagine him tamed down. There's nothing really stable about him; he's one of those people who talk about the established order of things, but never try it."

"He had the decency to marry my daughter, when she would have been compromised if he hadn't."

"How do you know he married her? He told you? That's great evidence, isn't it?"

"It's no evidence at all, but I believe him," said Helen. "I don't like him, but he tells the truth."

"Well, I'm sorry for their children," said Eteoneus. "It will be the greatest race of reformers that was ever invented."

"I take it you are going to stay," said Helen, "and I'm happier over the prospect than I've been in a long time."

"I didn't say I'd stay," said Eteoneus.

"But you will, won't you?" said Helen.

"Don't you think I'm too old?"

"Not a bit! You will soon be in your prime as a gate-keeper—you know all about men, and an extraordinary lot about women, and you can now act on your knowledge, to the great advantage of all of us. And whether you were old or not, Menelaos and I should want you to stay. We shall love our friends at any age."

"If you put it that way," said Eteoneus, "there doesn't seem to be so much point in going. I shall keep my prejudices, of course."

"Of course," said Helen. "What would a man be without his prejudices?"

"The going to Troy wasn't so bad," said Eteoneus,—

"As the coming back," said Helen. "We understand each other, Eteoneus. Thank you for staying, and thank you for this talk. If you ever have anything to say that you feel would be helpful to me, come and tell me."

"I will," said Eteoneus. "I've enjoyed this talk. Menelaos and I always disagree. Shall I tell him I'm staying, or will you?"

"Neither of us," said Helen. "Just stay. If you tell

him you are going to, he'll ask you why, and you won't
have a good reason unless you say I asked you to, and
then he may discharge you. Stay with us, Eteoneus,
without words, and I think the house will be at peace."

V

"THIS is as good a place to stop as any," said Orestes. "The view is very fine from this bend in the road, and the shade of this lonely tree is welcome. I've had my eye on it for the last half-mile. If I had known how heavy your father's supplies would prove, I would have declined at least half of them."

"We needn't walk much farther to-day," said Hermione. "What's the use of hurrying on as if we were afraid of being late somewhere? We aren't going to any particular place, and it makes no matter when we arrive. My, but I'm tired!"

"Now, don't lose your courage!" said Orestes. "The main reason for moving on is that no one seems eager to have us stop. That house last night barely put up with us—I was fearful to the end that they'd risk the sin of inhospitality, and invite us to try some other door."

"The trouble is, they've all heard about you," said Hermione. "You have as wide a reputation as my mother. They are afraid you'll murder them in their sleep. Poor Orestes!"

"Partly," said Orestes, "but when they see a woman along, they immediately conclude that you are not formally my wife. I suppose they think no one would marry me permanently. They don't like to take in women who are not strictly married or unmarried."

"Isn't it strange how people will miss the essentials,"

said Hermione, "and fasten on the mere formalities! If I had brought a marriage certificate with me, they would be cordial, but without it they are frigid. Yet I couldn't be more your wife than I am, even if there had been no ceremony at all."

"I feel thoroughly married myself," said Orestes. "Homeless, but domesticated. I wonder who is calling on your mother about this time."

"What made you think of her?"

"No compulsion at all," said Orestes. "I find it comes natural. Walking up that hill, when you were too much out of breath for conversation, I was going over some of the things she said, and what I intended to say if we had met again. Hermione, I accepted your father's offer of reconciliation in as ugly a mood as I have had toward him. I wouldn't have done it but for you!"

"It was too bad, the way it turned out," said Hermione. "You wanted to devote those last minutes to mother. I'm sure she was disappointed too, she has so few opportunities for the kind of talk she likes."

"To spend an hour on Menelaos when it might have been Helen!" said Orestes. "She has a fine mind, but it's undisciplined. She is very acute in her perceptions, but as far as I could observe, she follows them to no logical end. About the difference between error and sin, and about repenting only in advance, she's essentially right, but she declines to give those ideas a social application."

"How wise you are," said Hermione. "What do you mean?"

"Why, she talks as though society were only a name for a group of human beings, and as though each human

being were the important thing, whereas we know now
that 'human being' is just a term for the social atom.
Until that talk with her, I never understood what you
told me of her love-of-life theory, but it's perfectly plain
now; she's interested in the happiness of the individual,
and there is no sound reason why any individual should
be happy. She ought to be concerned for the welfare of
society. It's odd that she and I should have come together, for we have been working on principles diamet-
rically opposed. You can't hold aloof from your fellows
and be an individual, as she tries to be; you've got to take
your place in society, as I try to. Repenting in advance
is all very well for the egotist, but for the socially-minded
it's meaningless. You've got to punish crime and reward
virtue, if you feel any responsibility for keeping the world
going. She hardly is aware of such ideas, I should say,
and Menelaos is a bit blind to them too."

"Will you open that smaller wallet?" said Hermione.
"No, father is not socially-minded, but his individual biscuits are serviceable."

"The hopeful thing to me," said Orestes, "is that her
mind runs on ethical theory. It's a promising sign, even
though her view of the subject is limited and personal.
You observed, I suppose, that her theories all throw light
on her own conduct. I should call that a meager result.
You can't get very far in modern ethics unless you approach it as a social problem. One man on a desert island
would be neither good nor bad."

"Oh, you don't understand her at all!" said Hermione.
"Your own account of what she said makes it clearer to
me than it evidently is to you. I'm sure mother would
reply to any such illustration as that, that a single apple

on a desert island would be either a good apple or a bad one, and the same with a single man. And if society wasn't there to appreciate the apple, or if society was there and didn't appreciate the man, so much the worse for society."

"Of course that reply would occur to a half-baked mind," said Orestes. "Unless society were there with its standards and judgments, how would you know what is a good or a bad apple? Some like them greenish, some rather mellow."

"You don't mean that right and wrong are a matter of opinion!" said Hermione. "I side with mother. I think there is such a thing as a good apple. I wish we had one. . . . Orestes! If right and wrong are a matter of opinion, then you weren't absolutely right in—in what you did. You only thought you were!"

"I thought I was, and still think so," said Orestes, "and the chief reason I think so is that I was following the opinion of the best society about revenge."

"But not about filial duty," said Hermione.

"You haven't your mother's good sense, nor her tact," said Orestes. "I had to choose between two social duties, in a case where either choice would be wrong. It had to be, as I said, a matter of opinion."

"If either choice would have been wrong, there may be something the matter with those social duties, don't you think?"

"Hermione, what's done is done, and you only add to my unhappiness by such questions. You should have talked this way beforehand, or not at all!"

"That's mother's idea," said Hermione. "It does help, doesn't it?"

"I don't think it's quite the same idea," said Orestes. "I didn't mean to quote your mother."

"Try one of father's biscuits," said Hermione.

"Coming back to where we got off the subject," said Orestes, "it's the same way with beauty. Some people say that beauty is a positive thing, a kind of possession. You've noticed the remark about certain women, that they have great beauty. Of course that's wrong. Beauty is simply an effect—the effect of extreme approval—a matter of opinion. When we are wiser we shall say that such women are beautiful, not that they have beauty, or better still, we'll say they make the favorable impression called beauty."

"Mother won't mind," said Hermione. "So long as she always creates the same impression, the gift will be absolute enough for her."

"But does she always?" said Orestes. "I've met her only once, you know."

"Yes, I know," said Hermione. "But the oftener you look at her, the more it will be so."

"I'd like to see that for myself," said Orestes.

"But aren't there buildings, and landscapes, and things, which always excite the same opinion in people, or so nearly always that you think there's something peculiar about the people who don't like them?"

"What if there are?"

"Well, I should say that if they always make the same effect, there may be something constant in them, something in the proportions, perhaps, or the colors, which you might call beauty. I wish I had mother's coloring."

"You may say just as easily that there is something universal in human nature. Your mother has had her career because she has certain physical proportions which you call beauty, or because—"

"Or because men are all alike!" said Hermione. "I get your point now. Shall we walk on? I don't see a house on the horizon."

"There's one seven miles ahead, if that man was a good judge of distance," said Orestes. "We'll make it by nightfall."

"I couldn't walk so far if my life depended on it," said Hermione. "Can't we sleep out to-night, in some cave or shelter or something? I've heard of it's being done."

"Have you heard of any cave in the neighborhood?" said Orestes. "That's the point. The country is all flat rocks and sunlight, so far as I can see. Let's walk till you want to stop, and we'll decide then what to do next."

"Orestes, this can't go on, day after day. We shall perish. I try to be cheerful, but I'm giving out."

"You're all right, Hermione," said Orestes. "You're a bit over-tired, and perhaps the strain of that reception we got last evening has told on you. A night in the open air is just what we want. At least we can get away from people. We could be perfectly happy, you and I, if it weren't for the people we have to meet."

"Well, I'll try it a little farther."

He got the bundles on his shoulder and started off, and she followed slowly. When they had gone half a mile or so, he turned around and faced her.

"There's another striking thing about your mother," he said. "Have you noticed that whenever she addresses you—"

VI

"MENELAOS," said Eteoneus, "I think I've done your wife some injustice, and I'd like to retract several things I said of her—we needn't recall them. I've been talking with her."

"You mean you've been looking at her," said Menelaos. "I quite understand, and your apology is accepted. She has a persuading appearance. You are not the first."

VII

OF ALL the heroes who fought at Troy, Odysseus was the last to get home. In vain his wife expected him, and Telemachus, his young son, watching the family fortune as it dwindled, wondered if he were the head of the house, and if he ought to do something about it. The suitors were asking Penelope to marry them, on the assumption that Odysseus was dead or ought to be, and they were advancing their plea for her hand by economic pressure, living on her bounty till she should make up her mind. Helen had her suitors at the beginning of her life, Penelope at the end, when she was no longer young, and her beauty had never been more than, as Orestes would say, a matter of opinion. This fact has led some wise men to suppose that Penelope's story, as we now have it, by some accident got told backward. However that may be, the question remains why the suitors wanted to marry her anyway. For the property, Telemachus thought; and to his inexperienced eyes it seemed vast wealth. But Ithaca was a rocky barren place. The first time he traveled, he had his eyes opened. Since the annoying suitors came from a distance, they must have known better. Just what was in their minds we can only guess, but that they did besiege poor Penelope there is no doubt, for when Odysseus returned at last he drew his bow and slew them, every one.

At one point the story of Telemachus and his absent

father is touched with a memory of Helen, of some value as a picture of her on the domestic side.

Just before Odysseus made his dramatic reappearance, Telemachus had grown desperate. He resolved to slip away by night in a small boat, with a few trusted men, and sail to Pylos, where Nestor lived, and then on possibly to Sparta, the home of Menelaos. If either of his father's friends could give encouraging news of the missing man, he would return and wait patiently for another year. But if they gave him any positive reason to think that Odysseus was dead, he would go back to Ithaca, put on a bold front, celebrate his father's funeral, marry off his mother to somebody, he didn't care which one, send the other suitors away, and take charge of the house.

He had never left his father's island before. When he came to Pylos, he found Nestor just sitting down to a feast, with all his people around him. Telemachus was disposed to go home. He hadn't his father's gift for oratory, and he was embarrassed to walk up to Nestor and state his errand before the public gaze. But he reminded himself in what a good cause he came, and fortunately Nestor insisted that he should eat before he talked. After the meal the old man opened the conversation himself. He belonged to that rough early time that Eteoneus had lived in. He asked the boy if he was out on some errand of honest merchandise, or if he was operating as a pirate. Telemachus was a little frightened at the question, but he caught the idea, and let the old man think that pirating was one of his favorite sports, or would be when he had more practise.

"But I've come to ask if you have any news at all of my father. We have heard nothing at home, for I've for-

gotten how many years, and we've reached the point
where even bad news would be better than this ominous
silence. We understand that Menelaos is safely home
again, and that Agamemnon got home, but not safely.
Ajax is dead, we understand, and we have other items
about my father's friends, but not a single word of him,
though he was a famous man, with a gift for exciting
comment. If he had been killed, I should think some one
would have told us. Where in the world is he? Will you
tell me how and when you saw him last, and anything you
know about him since? If the facts are bad, don't soften
them; I'd like the truth."

Nestor went off into reminiscences. Odysseus was
his best friend. He never would tire of remembering
their exploits together on the plains of Troy. Telemachus
was afraid he wouldn't.

"But when it came to our returning," he said, "none
of us was wise. It began the day after the city fell. How
we did celebrate! Then, if you please, Agamemnon called
the host together to sacrifice! To say truth, most of us
were carrying a good deal of wine. Then Menelaos said
he was going home at once—the war was over and there
was nothing to stay for. Agamemnon insisted on some
further sacrifices, to appease Athena. Rather foolish of
him, I must say, for if a goddess is angry with you, she's
angry, and sacrifice is a waste of time, among other
things. They talked back and forth at each other, but
what they said I couldn't hear; while they were arguing
the rest of us had got excited, and there was the greatest
din you ever heard, outside of a real fight. We took sides
about equally—half of us were for sailing, and half were
for more sacrifices. I saw it the same way as Menelaos,

and we made up quite a fleet when we set out the next day. But in the morning air we found ourselves sober again, and as we sailed on we grew thoughtful. It was the reaction, I suppose. When we had gone as far as Tenedos, most of us stopped for a few hours and offered sacrifices, to be on the safe side, but Menelaos went on, or he had dropped out of the convoy; we saw no more of him. Your father made us quite a speech. He argued that if sacrifices were the thing after all, he was for no half-way measures, and he turned back to rejoin Agamemnon. And that's the last I saw of him. Not a word have I heard since. Most of the others reached their homes. In Lesbos I stopped to sacrifice again, to make sure, and I must say we had a great wind right into the harbor. Idomeneus—did you ever hear of him? The suitor Helen turned down first—he had the smoothest trip of all, without losing a man, and he's back in Crete as though nothing had happened. But that was a nasty trick Ægisthus played on Agamemnon! You've heard, of course, how Orestes took his revenge? That's the advantage of having a son—to see that your murderer gets his deserts. Odysseus is fortunate, I don't mind saying, in a boy as enterprising as you seem to be. He'll come home, if he isn't killed, and if he is killed, you'll go after the man who did it. Unless it was the work of providence, of course."

Telemachus was disappointed. No news of his father, and apparently no chance of any, not even from Menelaos. But his curiosity extended to other matters also; he was young. "We heard what Ægisthus did to Agamemnon," he said, "but only in the vaguest sort of way. We had none of the particulars."

"Well," said Nestor, "that was a remarkable case, if you consider what a man Agamemnon was, and how little Ægisthus amounted to. As it came to me, Ægisthus plotted the whole thing, and he intended to kill Menelaos too, if he had gone to Mycenae. Clytemnestra wasn't so bad. She held out against the idea for a long time, and Ægisthus would never have persuaded her if he hadn't first got rid of the minstrel. You know about the minstrel? Agamemnon left him as the special protector of his wife. Whether it was the effect of his playing—he played and sang every evening—or whether it was the influence of his inspired character, Ægisthus could make no headway with Clytemnestra so long as the minstrel was there. So he asked him to go fishing one day, and the minstrel went to keep an eye on him, and Ægisthus marooned him on a rock that is covered at high water. Clytemnestra gave in at once. The thought of his sins drove Ægisthus to sacrificing; he was always at his prayers, till Clytemnestra worried over the loss of cattle. He was praying when Orestes found him. Menelaos stayed at home, by the inspiration of the gods, and so escaped his brother's fate. He's at Sparta now, you know, with Helen. She's lovelier than ever, they say."

Telemachus said that Sparta would be his next stopping-place. Perhaps Menelaos might know something of his father. Nestor thought not, but it would do no harm to inquire. So the young man continued his voyage, hoping for news, and not unmoved by the prospect of seeing Helen, said to be more beautiful than ever.

When he came to the famous gate where once Paris had knocked, Eteoneus held him up with some feeble excuse, and hurried to find Menelaos.

"There's another handsome young man outside," he said. "Do we let him in?"

"Eteoneus," said Menelaos, "there have been times in your life when you did not act like a fool. I wish I could say this was one of them. I don't get the reference. Of course we let him in! When I have traveled in the past, I have always been hospitably entertained, and I dare say it has happened to you. We must do the same in our turn, when a traveler comes."

"Now, what's the meaning of that!" said Eteoneus, but not very loud.

Telemachus had seen no such house as this. The roof was high, and somehow the smoke got out and the light got in; you would think the sun or the moon was shining. The size and the wealth of it embarrassed him. He remembered that his father had more brains, but the thought didn't bring ease of manner. They took him to the marble baths, where the attendants embarrassed him further by the thorough washing they gave him, and they oiled his hair, and put on him better clothes than he was accustomed to. Menelaos came to welcome him, a tall man with beautiful long, dark locks, which needed no oil to make them shine. He wasn't so impressive as his house. It occurred to Telemachus that he was beginning to miss his daily exercise at Troy; he was of a full habit. At the feast which Menelaos ordered for the guest, he showed that loss of exercise does not diminish appetite.

"I've never seen a house like this," said Telemachus, "and though I haven't traveled far, I doubt if there's another such in the world. All this bronze and gold and amber, to say nothing of the silver and ivory! The court of Zeus himself on Olympus must be like this—it can't be much finer."

Menelaos put on a sober air, and said that no one ought to compare himself to the gods, but it certainly was a satisfactory house. That is, the building.

"But I would exchange a large part of my wealth," he said, "to have back the years I spent away from this house, and the friends of mine who died at Troy, or were lost on the way home. Of course, we all have to die some-time, and I dare say many of them would now be in their graves anyway, even if there had been no Troy. But I'm sorry for one friend in particular—for Odysseus. You must have heard the name. He did more than any of the others for me, and here I am home again, and nobody knows where he is, or whether he is alive at all. I dare say his old father has a broken heart, and his wife, and that infant son of his, who must be growing up now."

The mention of his father brought sudden anguish to Telemachus, sudden because he had had his thoughts on Menelaos' fine house. He was about to reveal his name and his errand, when Helen entered from her vaulted room. How could it be? Yet it could be no other! His mother had been careful to tell him how old Helen was, and he knew what she had been through. He had expected Aphrodite, a sophisticated goddess, charm-ing as sin. As she walked toward him he saw that she was young and maidenly, and he knew what Artemis must be like. With her came a girl who seemed older but probably wasn't. They called her Adraste. She set a chair for Helen, with a footstool, and brought her the wool for spinning in a golden basket set on wheels. Tele-machus forgot his father, forgot his mother, forgot the suitors. All his life he tried to be sorry he forgot, but he never was.